Older Than My Mother

OLDER THAN MY MOTHER

A Nurse's Life and Triumph Over Breast Cancer

Augusta Hicks Gale

Ananse Press
Seattle

Copyright © 1996 by Ananse Press

All rights reserved

Manufactured in the United States of America

Gale, Augusta Hicks, 1941 –
    Older than my mother: a nurse's life and triumph
    over breast cancer / Augusta Hicks Gale.
        p. cm.

Includes bibliographical references and index.

ISBN 0-9605670-8-9 (hardcover)

    1.   Gale, Augusta Hicks, 1941–Health
    2.   Breast–Cancer–Patients–United States–Biography.
    3.   Afro-American nurses–United States–Biography.
    4.   Health services administrators–United States–Biography.

I. Title

RC280.B8G326 1996

616.99' 449' 009–dc20

[B]

                                        96-18873
                                           CIP

Ananse Press offers a cassette tape of the book. For information write
to Ananse Press, P. O. Box 22565, Seattle, WA 98122

Dedication

This book is dedicated to all women and men who have been diagnosed with breast cancer, and to the thousands who have lost their lives to the disease. It is further dedicated to all sufferers of catastrophic illnesses and to those who have empowered themselves by becoming advocates for their health care.

ACKNOWLEDGEMENTS

I wish to acknowledge the unrelenting support and love of my family – my father, the Rev. Perry Hicks, who died this spring, my stepmother Dorothy Wesley Hicks, my brothers Henry and Perry Hicks, my sister-in-law Ann Alexander Hicks, my niece Annette Hicks, my aunt Mattie Hicks and my aunt Eula Mae Hasson. I have been cheered on by my son, Byron Berry, who still thinks his "Mommie" is the greatest. All of them demonstrated much love, affection, and concern about my health. My church family, the Zion Baptist Church in Lynn, Massachusetts, continues to pray for me and has been a warm and continuous support. Thanks, too, to Delores Harris and Virginia Peacock, who have been at my "beck and call" to assist me in any manner they can. I would be remiss should I not thank Gladys, Ken, and Mae Odom who opened their home and fed me so that I could concentrate on writing this book.

Georgia Stewart McDade toiled over the original manuscript to bring some order to the story. Barbara Laners brought her own experiences with breast cancer to a critical reading of the manuscript. Jill Wiske graciously read and rendered a candid appraisal of the manuscript. Thanks, too, to Zola Mumford who travelled from Seattle to Boston to record portions of the manuscript for a taped edition.

CONTENTS

PREFACE

A diagnosis of cancer or any other catastrophic illness makes a person stop and think about his or her life. Naturally the diagnosis and treatment occupy most of one's thoughts until the illness is brought under control. In the time that follows, however, reassessments and recollections fill the mind. It is from such a period of reflection in my own life that this story comes.

One in every eight American women – approximately 182,000 – will be diagnosed with breast cancer this year. It is the most common kind of cancer among all women in the country and one of the leading causes of cancer deaths of African American women of all ages, and the toll from breast cancer among African American women continues to rise.

With two bouts of cancer behind me, in the middle of my fifth decade of life, I am a person who has had many experiences, and I have learned much from these experiences. This book is an attempt to record some of the defining aspects of my life, particularly that of breast cancer, and my coping methods. My hope is that my findings may be of assistance to other people facing similar circumstances.

From my family, which included two mothers, one of whom died of breast cancer, and people I have known along the way, I have developed my sense of self. Savoring life is now part of my daily existence.

My Mother, Oleary Hasson Hicks, about 1940

Chapter 1
The Unwelcome Visitor

Why, at age fifty, did my mother die from metastatic breast cancer? She survived her surgery a mere six months. At forty-seven I was diagnosed with breast cancer. This is a story about the intersection of cancer with my past, present, and, unknown future. As such it follows the way I live and think about my life, what meanings this illness has on how I see my future, what past experiences and long-term knowing has to do with how I perceive this unwelcome visitor in my present, and what visions of the future I am now able to entertain because of it.

I do not want to be a statistic. Studies and surveys indicate that the incidence of breast cancer in black women is much lower than for white women; however, black women die of it at a much greater rate. Some doctors hypothesize that death comes so quickly and so often because black women probably do not seek proper medical care, that by the time they are diagnosed, the cancer in the breast has metastasized to the vital organs in the body. Perhaps this is true for some women, but at this time there is no single explanation. The verdict is still out.

What I have had to do and how I have had to manage because of breast cancer have not always been easy or pleasant. But the diagnosis had been made. Two mornings after being told I had cancer, I was walking in the Salem Commons. I wanted to walk alone. I needed to walk alone, to be with and by myself for a while. But of all mornings, one of the women who lived in my rooming house had also gotten up early. "Augusta, I'll go walking with you," she said. I did not want that. But I wanted even less to tell her that I wanted to walk alone. Quick thinking made me decide to walk very fast, fast enough to tire my friend. I knew she would be unable to keep up, she would sit down, and blessedly, she would tell me to go ahead.

Sure enough, I took off like a bat out of hell! We walked a lap, and she said, "Oh, Augusta, I can't keep up with you. I'll wait here until you come back this way, and then I'll join you." I said that was fine.

I started walking. Soon I was crying. That was the first emotional release I had after the news. I just walked and cried. I don't know why I was crying. I wasn't saying anything, just crying, crying, crying. And by the time I would walk back around to where my neighbor was waiting, I would just stop crying, and she said, "Oh, I'm still resting. I can't keep up with you." That was fine with me, and I proceeded to walk, and to cry, again. I walked for six miles, and I cried for six miles. On the second lap I had said to myself, "Why are you crying?" I could not answer that. I had no answer. I didn't know why I was crying. One of the concerns I had was the fact that I would be going through this alone. I was in a new setting. I had just relocated in the New England area and did not know anyone. I didn't have family here. I probably came to the conclusion that I felt sorry for myself. "You're going to have your breast removed. For forty-seven years it has been a part of you, and now it's going to be removed. It's like a part of you dying." I think I was more afraid of how I would look and what people would say than I was of death. I had been so much identified with my breasts. I began to wonder if I would still be attractive.

After I had let the tears and crying play out, I asked myself, "What do I need to do now?" The part of me that was an experienced nurse calmly said, "Get the proper treatment." I realized that I needed to educate myself about all of the possibilities, the options available. And I knew that I needed to move forward immediately. The person I became and the information I gathered may help others in similar situations. When I received my diagnosis, I did not know one woman of color who had this disease. I certainly knew no one who had had a mastectomy. My hope is that my journey will serve as a steppingstone for others so that they will not feel this isolation.

I did not experience denial of my cancer diagnosis. Once it was diagnosed, my concern was getting the proper treatment. I needed to educate myself about all the possibilities, the options. In order to get the very best care that I could get I needed to advocate for myself. So I started to move in that direction. Once I began to take those steps, I was more comfortable with the diagnosis and felt more confident in my own power to do what I could do.

Sure, I was losing my breast, and there was some grief. I was losing a part of my body. I did not get angry that my breasts had "failed" me. I did not think of my breasts as having developed something causing me pain and anger and suffering. I did not have that kind of attitude. I reminded myself to focus on getting the very best care and moving on with my life.

Early on I started exploring the positive aspects of having a mastectomy: I would not have the trenches in my shoulder from holding up a double F breast. (I still, to this day, have those deep trenches in my shoulders.) I would be able to wear blouses that buttoned in the front without pinning them to keep them fastened because they always stood open. Before the surgery all my blouses and dresses opened in the back or side. I would be comfortably able to wear suits or blazers because I could now fasten them. My neck and shoulders wouldn't hurt anymore from the weight of my breasts. I concentrated on these positives. I just started turning everything I thought was negative into something positive and meaningful to me. And I think that's what really helped me to get through this crisis.

I "collaborated" with myself. Had I known an African American woman who had had a similar experience, I certainly would have reached out to that person, just to talk with her. But I did not know such a person, so I was self-directed, trying to do the very best thing I could for myself. In the process I learned a lot, and I have been able to share with others.

This drawing shows a woman performing a breast self examination. Regular monthly examinations enabled me to become so familiar with my breasts that I was able to detect a change from one month to the next which, in my case, indicated breast cancer. Illustration by Eric Salisbury.

Chapter 2
Moving Forward

During the next three months I continued to work every day. I was able to get up every morning and pray and meditate about what was happening to me. I would walk in the Salem Commons just to be alone. I worked eight hours a day and did not share my diagnosis with anyone. I would see other patients being admitted with a diagnosis of breast cancer. I wanted so very much to reach out just to see how they were coping and to see them again immediately after surgery.

I had a very close working relationship with the nurses I supervised in Continuing Care at Salem Hospital. I wanted to prepare my staff for what was happening with me, but everyday I would procrastinate about sharing with them. Dot, Carol, Linda, Joan, Lillian, Peggy, and Penny, the secretary. Which one would I select to share this with? I chose Linda. I don't know why. Perhaps she was just there at that moment.

I called Linda into my office to tell her that I had a cancerous tumor in my breast and that I was going to have a mastectomy. Initially there was silence, then, "Augusta, how could you keep this to yourself?" I guess I didn't want anyone to feel sorry for me.

During one of our staff meetings I informed the entire staff of my situation. I felt relieved that I had done so. I was now ready to move forward.

I even went to Buffalo, New York, to a big hospital discharge planner's convention. As I met new people and learned more about discharge planning, I didn't think about my diagnosis. The last day of the convention, I became sad as I began to think about my upcoming trip to New York to the Cancer Center. When I returned to Salem, I got ready to go to Memorial Sloan-Kettering Cancer Center in New York where the operation would be performed.

I had discovered the lump in my breast through self-examination. I knew my breasts. I had examined them in November of 1987. I had not detected a lump then. But in December 1987 I discovered a lump. I did not panic. I had a mammogram, and the lump appeared to be nonmalignant. I was disturbed, and I knew that I should go and have it checked.

In January 1988, I examined my breast again. The lump was still there. It had not disappeared, and I said, "Well, I need to have a biopsy to find out if it's benign or malignant." I knew that something was wrong.

I did not rush to have a mastectomy that very day. I needed time to think about what was going to happen to me, to explore the options. I needed time to empower myself. I believe the outcome was to my advantage.

Because I was new in Salem, I did not know the hospitals, and I didn't know what I was going to do. I looked in the phone directory and saw Brigham and Women's Hospital in Boston and selected it simply because of its name. The person with whom I spoke on the phone said it is an excellent hospital. So I went there and had the biopsy, which is not a painful procedure, but I could feel the tugging and pulling. I did not want to be uncomfortable, so I asked to be put to sleep. The results came back as *carcinoma in situ* - a precancerous tumor that often develops into invasive cancer.

I was terribly disappointed with the way I was treated by the physician I had there. After he did the biopsy, he telephoned me to let me know the results. For all he knew, I could have fainted there alone. I thought it was unethical and unprofessional for a physician to telephone me to say the tumor is malignant: "You have cancer." If we had discussed sharing the test outcome over the telephone, that would have been fine with me, but since I didn't expect him to call me and give me the news over the telephone, I was shocked. So it was there I became an advocate for myself. I went in immediately to talk with him to make sure about the diagnosis. His distance and coldness made me conclude that I could not form a relationship with this physician because he only saw me as a number and a diagnosis. But I continued to listen. I moved closer to him to listen more carefully. And this doctor pulled his chair away as I got closer to him! He confirmed what I had thought earlier. Worse, I didn't like the three choices he gave me. First, he could do a bilateral mastectomy. That was the furthest thing from my mind at that point. I didn't even want to hear that. Second, he could send me to the radiologist. "Don't send me," I was thinking; "Collaborate, conference, and see what you can do. Discuss the treatment plan, my options, and include me in the plan." Or, third, he could "do nothing and just watch" me. I was completely thrown. My observation made me think he was not committed to me. Under no circumstances would I submit to his "wait and see" approach.

There was no doubt in my mind as to whether the diagnosis was incorrect or not, but I spoke with a physician in New York who had performed cancer surgery on one of the bones in my leg in 1984 and asked him to refer me to a breast surgeon, and he did. I went back to New York for a second opinion for treatment, and I was comfortable with the outcome. The cancer was in the upper outer aspect of my right breast where most such cancers occur. That area has the most breast tissue. The doctor had all of my laboratory reports because he wanted to confirm the diagnosis of cancer.

The trip from Boston to New York was like going from hell to heaven. When I arrived, I felt as if the nurses had their arms outstretched and the doctor was waiting for me. The approach to me, as a patient, was as different as day is from night. I received individualized treatment. The doctor sat down and talked with me. He said that the pathologist in New York agreed with the diagnosis of the Boston pathologist. "Now, there are options in your treatment," he told me. "In view of the fact that you're in

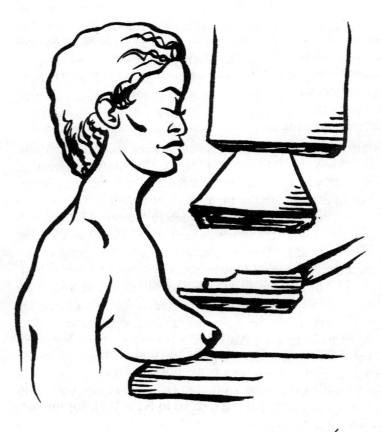

This drawing shows a woman getting a mammogram, a simple, occasionally uncomfortable, but painless x-ray of the breast which can detect early breast cancers sometimes as much as two years before they can be felt. The earlier the detection, the greater the chance of survival. Illustration by Eric Salisbury.

the high risk category – your age, your family history (your mother died of metastatic breast cancer) – we could do a unilateral mastectomy removing only one breast, or we could do a bilateral mastectomy removing both breasts. And the reason we would want to do a bilateral mastectomy is because there's a thirty per cent chance that the cancer would appear in the other breast according to your diagnosis."

I made the decision at that time to have a bilateral mastectomy. As a matter of fact, when the doctor finished examining me and gave me the options, I was ready to be admitted to the hospital that day to have the surgery. I was that confident in that physician. He was quite concerned with my decision, pointing out to me that my left breast was perfectly normal.

In addition to wanting to reduce the odds of developing cancer in the other breast, I chose a bilateral mastectomy for another reason: I was going to have my breast reconstructed. I knew it would have been impossible to reconstruct a double F breast without doing reduction surgery in the other breast. I said, "Well, if they're going to do reduction surgery, I might as well start at zero." So I chose the bilateral mastectomy.

The doctor told me how much time I could safely delay the surgery. I postponed it for a little while and returned to Salem because I wanted to attend the convention in Buffalo. After my return I packed everything, including fiery red nail polish, satin pillow cases and pretty pajamas, to go to New York for the surgery. I had just met my boyfriend, Arnold Howe, and he was very, very reassuring and supportive of me. This really helped me to adjust and to become more emotionally stable.

After packing, I sat on my bed nervously waiting for Sloan-Kettering to call to let me know that there was a bed available. When the phone rang, I answered it quickly, but I wasn't prepared for what I heard. "This is Memorial Sloan-Kettering Cancer Center calling for Augusta Gale. We cannot admit you today because you do not have insurance." Ouch! I had made a decision with which I was comfortable. I was packed. I was ready to go. Now, here was this call telling me that I would not be admitted. So, I began to cry.

When I transferred to Massachusetts from Kentucky, someone failed to transfer my insurance. Under the Consolidated Omnibus Budget Reconciliation Act, better known as COBRA, employees leaving one job are covered for a period of time, and the new employer is supposed to let the employee know when that period expires. I thought this had been done, and it hadn't.

I sat there not knowing one single person in Salem except Arnold, whom I had just met, and some fellow employees. Whom could I call? With whom could I speak? I don't know why, but Nancy Reagan came to mind. I reasoned she could help me. She's been through this. She'll know what I'm going through. I'll call her.

I picked up the phone and called Information for the White House. I dialed the number. "May I speak with Nancy Reagan, please?"

"President Reagan's wife?"

I said, "Yes. Her name is Nancy; is it not?" So I got through about two secretaries, and I told them what the problem was.

"Oh no. You need to speak with her private secretary." So I got her private secretary on the line and told her what the problem was.

She said, "Don't worry. You will get in that hospital today. If we have to call Health and Human Services that regulate insurance, we'll get you in there today. Just call your doctor and tell him there'll be a little delay, but you'll get there." I hung up the phone and continued to cry.

In about ten minutes the phone rang. "Augusta Gale?"

"Yes."

"Sloan Kettering. We have a bed for you." I picked up my suitcase and headed out the door to catch the shuttle plane to New York. My friend Arnold drove me to the airport in a limo, so I could be comfortable, he said.

I tell this story to encourage other women to do everything in their power to seek the best medical care that they can find, and they are likely to be successful in finding the best treatment available.

I'm one of few women in the world who has had three breast sizes. I went from a double F cup to zero cup when both breasts were removed, then to a C cup after reconstruction. There aren't many women with those changes in measurements. Before surgery I was a double F cup, thirty-six or thirty-eight. In fact, some of my friends called me the "Black Dolly Parton." People would see my breasts coming before they saw me. People who didn't know my name would refer to me as, "You know, your friend with the big boobs, the one with the big 'you know.' " That's how they would describe me.

I did have some anxiety, some concerns about how I would look, what people would say. I did not want people saying, "Oh, she had breast cancer; she had her breast removed. She's not a woman anymore." Yes, such thoughts did go through my mind.

It's strange how certain encounters you have had in life surface at various times. At this time I recalled what a young man told me when I was in high school. He said, "If you didn't have those big boobs I wouldn't look at you, and neither would any other man." I suspect he made this statement because I was very adamant about not having a sexual relationship with him or any other person until I was ready. Now, for a second I had flashbacks to this incident, but only for a short period of time.

When I got to Sloan-Kettering, the mother of Frank Saldo, one of my colleagues from New Jersey, was at the hospital having a mastectomy. Her husband was there, and Frank had told him that I was coming. Soon after entering the waiting room, I was approached by his father who asked if I were from Boston. When I answered yes, he asked if I were Augusta Gale. He said, "I'm Frank's father. We have been expecting you. My wife is here, and she just had the surgery." At this time I wanted to go see somebody who had just had a mastectomy. I went to her room, and we talked. She was a beautiful woman, and to this day we're still in touch.

Chapter 3
No One Is Immune

No one is immune from breast cancer. When I was admitted, I was placed in the room with a young woman in her late twenties. Among the subjects we discussed was how we felt about having a mastectomy. The next morning, it was time for surgery. She left first. After her unilateral mastectomy she had one side with full range of motion. Then I went down. Both my breasts were removed, and on the right side I had a radical mastectomy. My lymph nodes were removed, so I had limited range of motion on my right side. But on my left side I had a simple mastectomy. All the breast tissue was removed, but the lymph nodes were not. Thus I had a full range of motion in my left hand. I thought I was going to be in a lot of pain when I woke up in the recovery room after about eight hours of surgery, but the nerves had been cut, and I was just numb. In the afternoon we both returned to our room. The nurses were in and out much of the day and night providing the necessary intensive care for us.

The next morning my roommate said, "I want to shampoo my hair."

I said, "Okay. Let's get up and shampoo your hair."

"No, Augusta. We can't do that. We just had surgery."

I said, "There's nothing wrong with your right arm. Let's go in there and shampoo your hair." She got up and went into the bathroom.

"Put your hand up there, and I'll put mine here, and we'll work it." And we did.

I told my roommate we had to begin the healing of our bodies and feeling good about what we had been through and not let it interfere with the process. We got her hair shampooed, and we put on our makeup and fresh gowns. We polished our nails. When her family came to visit, they could hardly believe that we had had surgery the day before. And my family, of course, were just as surprised when they visited me. Both of us were cheerful and well groomed. I spread the good cheer and grooming around to the other patients. I polished their nails and got them out of bed. A group of us met to learn exercises to help our recovery. We climbed the wall with our fingertips, stretching to regain range of motion. We supported each other, and some of us still keep in touch.

About two o'clock in the morning after surgery I wanted something to eat. The hospital didn't have any graham crackers. So when my roommate's father came, she told him, "Oh Augusta was hungry, and I think she likes graham crackers." They must have had stock in graham crackers because her father went out and brought back ten boxes for me! Everyone who came into my room wanted to know if **I** had stock in the graham cracker company.

My roommate's family was very, very supportive of me in other ways, too. Whatever they brought in for her, they brought the same for me. The giving was reciprocal because I helped her and helped her mom get through the ordeal. Her mother would call me and say, "She's going to come home in a couple of days, and I'm not ready. I don't think I can handle it. I just don't know what to do." So I spoke with my roommate. No one had come to teach her the exercises she needed to do. I insisted that she not leave the hospital until someone went over the exercise regimen with her and she knew exactly what to expect. So she stayed there a bit longer, and her mother felt more comfortable about her coming home.

After the mastectomy, the doctor would come around to check our dressings. We had drainage tubes hanging everywhere. There was one doctor who came in and never pulled the privacy curtain. I don't know what objection he had to pulling it. The second time he came in, I said – I probably said it the first time –

"Please help me to understand your reason for not pulling the privacy curtain when you come in to change my dressing. Look at me."

He looked around. "Oh. There's nobody in the hallway. Nobody can see you," he said.

"That's not the point. I expect to have privacy, and I have a right to have it. Would you want to lie in that bed after having surgery on your penis and have someone expose you?"

"Of course not! Of course not."

I said, "The same here. I don't want it." So when this doctor would come to my room, the first thing he would do, before he would speak to me, was pull the privacy curtain.

When the other women and I would meet for our exercises in our support group, they would complain about this physician not pulling the privacy curtain. I said, "Did you tell him about it?"

"Oh, no."

I would say, "Why?"

Their answers were always that they did not want to do anything to make him angry because he might do something. Or he is the doctor, and I don't want to challenge the doctor.

I said, "Look. You have a right to privacy, and you should tell him to pull that curtain," but I don't think any of them ever challenged him about it.

Although I had no problems with the healing process, I was not discharged at the designated time that the hospital wanted to discharge me. I was going to recuperate at my brother's house, but he and his family had gone to Mexico for one of his in-law's graduation from medical school, and I did not want to be in the house alone. So I insisted on staying in the hospital. "Oh, no. You will have to leave," they said at the hospital.

I said, "I'll tell you what. If you discharge me, I will camp in the lobby of this hospital." I told them my reasons for wanting to stay there. "Now, if you insist on my leaving, I will leave, and I will call every newspaper and every television station in New

York City and have them come here to let them know how you've treated me." They changed their mind and kept me in the hospital.

Most people don't know it, but a patient can insist on staying. Hospitals use a set of guidelines – diagnostic related groups (DRGs). Each procedure or illness has a designated recuperation period. If there are no complications, a patient must leave at that time, or earlier, or a doctor may appeal the standard if complications arise. But hospitals collect the designated amount even if a patient leaves early. For example, if the DRG is three days, and the patient is discharged on day two, the hospital is paid for three days. Anyone who feels she needs to remain in the hospital should insist on staying. A patient should know the DRG for his or her procedure and demand to stay there and recuperate. This is empowerment.

The day I was discharged from the hospital was a very emotional one for me. I sat on the bed and cried. I felt quite comfortable in the hospital because every female patient I met had had a mastectomy and all our chests looked the same: flat. Now I was going out into society where I had to compete with other women with breasts, and I felt different because I didn't have breasts, but I constantly reminded myself that I was alive and feeling great.

The nurse brought my temporary prosthesis. To tell the truth, I must have stuffed a bale of cotton in that prosthesis because I wanted to look as I did when I walked in. I just knew that as soon as I walked out that door, everybody, everybody in New York would know I had had a mastectomy, including my cousin Jim Buckley, who came to pick me up. I said to myself, "I know he and everybody else is going to be looking and wondering, but I'm going to throw them off because they don't know if it's the right or left. They don't know that I had both breasts removed."

I began recuperation at the New York home of my brother Henry and his wife, Ann. A few days after I was discharged from the hospital, I went to a nightclub with them. We were sitting at the table when the waitress came over in a very low-cut dress. Her breasts looked as though they were sitting outside of her bodice. I looked at her, with all this exposure, and for the first time in my life, breasts were ugly to me. I turned to Ann and said, "Did I ever look like that?"

"Well, of course not," she answered.

I was still stuffed with a bale of cotton. When a young man approached me and was looking directly at my breasts as though he were admiring them I laughed to myself, and said, "Eat your heart out. You are looking and admiring cotton stuffed in a bra."

I stayed with Henry and Ann and commuted into New York City from Long Island twice a week to have fluid aspirated from my chest. (There is usually fluid build-up in the chest wall after a mastectomy). I was assured and comfortable enough with myself that I told the doctor that I could do the aspiration, but he said, "No, you can't."

"Oh, yes, I can," I told him, because I was that confident in myself and wanted to help myself and be a part of what was going on with me. But he insisted I come in and let him aspirate the fluid.

The first day I went to the doctor Ann insisted that I take a cab from Long Island into New York City so that no one on the train would bump into me and injure my chest. I gave in and took a cab. Once I got into the city the cab driver seemed to hit every pothole in the streets, and I would brace my chest with my purse to absorb some of the jolt. Finally I said, "Would you please take it easy. I have just had surgery, and this is a rough ride."

He replied, "Sure, why didn't you tell me. Sometimes a request asked is a request granted. Now, I did not return in a cab but rather took the train after I went shopping.

I'm used to taking care of and doing for myself. When a doctor confesses, "I'm terrible at giving injections," I give myself the injection. I do it because I'm not going to hurt myself. It has not been my experience to have the doctor resent my action. If he or she does, I still insist on giving my own injection.

Granted, an aspiration is a different, more complex procedure; it requires withdrawing fluid, and everything connected with it must be highly sterile. The chest cavity is numb from surgery. During a mastectomy little nerves and nerve endings are cut, and they take a while to regroup, so there's no feeling. When the needle is inserted and the fluid drawn out, the patient does not feel it. I didn't feel it. I felt pressure, but not pain, and I could have easily done it myself. Of course, there are nurses who would not do this.

Although chemotherapy or radiation therapy is often given as a follow-up treatment after mastectomies, my doctor deemed it unnecessary in my case; he believed these treatments might only increase my survival chances by three to five percent. I decided not to take either one. Depending on the stage of their cancer or their prospect of recovery, other people may require chemotherapy or radiation.

Chapter 4
Our Family, Ourselves

One of the benefits of my illness was its positive effects on relationships. The time with my brother was beneficial, and not only physically. Henry quickly associated what had happened to my mother with what was happening to me. He realized that both Mother and I were around the same age when my mother was diagnosed with breast cancer; my mom died in 1970, within a year after her diagnosis. I hastily assured him that the comparison might not be a good one, because of the difference in treatments during the 1970s and now. When Mother died, doctors

My last visit with my mother following her radical mastectomy in 1969.

The Christmas holiday I spent with my biological mother in California is one of my happiest memories.

were still performing the Halstead Procedure: they removed all of the breast, the lymph nodes, and the muscle in the chest. One side of her chest was deeply sunken, looking deformed. She adjusted well, and it didn't seem to depress her because she continued as usual. She even met a new boyfriend and enjoyed quality time with him.

My mother was not given any choices or options. She had what was called the "two-step surgery." She went in the hospital and had a biopsy. What was called a frozen section specimen was sent to the lab while she was still on the operating-room table. Her sample was malignant, so the next step was to do the mastectomy. I talked with her about it later and asked her how she felt about what was done. She said, "Well, I woke up, and I felt this large bandage on my chest, and I knew I had had my breast removed." My mother only lived about six months after she had the mastectomy.

I explained to Henry that my cancer was a new ball game. The technology is different. I performed breast self-examinations; I'm sure my mom never performed breast self-examination. "I discovered the lump early. I'm here for treatments," I told him, and he was comfortable with that. I realized how important it was that I be comfortable with the diagnosis, and how that was reflected in my interactions about it with members of my family and friends. Seeing me comfortable and taking charge, they felt comfortable talking with me and accepting the diagnosis of cancer.

The impact of the surgery on my son Byron, who was in the Marines at the time, is not quite clear. He did not express his feelings directly to me, but his wife twice informed me that he had said to her, "I wish I had been there for my mom when she had the surgery." His father and I had separated when Byron entered high school. While I had custody of him during the divorce proceedings, I gave him options, letting him know what might happen if he stayed with me and what might happen if he stayed with his father. He chose to live with his father whose rearing practices I supported as much as possible. Although he had attended private elementary school with its regimentation and discipline, he never made the carryover to high school. He was influenced by many distractions. He was handsome, and girls of every race, creed, and color were very interested in him, so interested, I felt, that he was not allotting adequate time to his studies. I did not want to interfere, but I did point this out to his father. Still my son neglected his studies. After graduation, he joined the Marines but after approximately two years wanted to leave. He finished his stint but never found time to go on to school as I had hoped.

Byron in his Marine Corps dress uniform, 1982

I do know he was excited about the June 1989 edition of *Ebony* magazine where I discussed my recovery from breast cancer. He took it to his base in California to show to the other Marines. When I went out to visit him, several of them complimented me on its excellence. I could see relief in Byron when he realized I was truly comfortable. For him, the article was the vehicle which allowed me to express my feelings. Byron commented several times about how good he felt about that article. So he was eventually able to accept what has happened and was very supportive of me afterwards.

My older brother, Perry, who lives in California, was not soothed despite my calm. He just couldn't deal with my having breast cancer. He had been around our mom more than I had, and he saw the same thing happening to me that had happened to her, and he just couldn't talk about it.

I kept these different responses in mind when I went to Ruston, Louisiana, to complete my recuperation with my parents. My father, who was blind, would come to my room every morning to speak to me and to assist me in any way he could. That did a world of good for me. His coming and greeting me every morning let me know that he cared. His concern gave me such a lift. To have my stepmom there, too, helping me with my exercises and preparing my favorite foods – chicken, greens and potato salad – was just marvelous.

Throughout the process, my family was extremely supportive in a variety of ways, even though it was very difficult for them. I had been forthright in breaking the news to my parents and my close family members. I remember calling home after the biopsy and my stepmother saying, "Oh, I'm going to pray that it's not cancer. I'm just gonna pray so hard."

At that time I was really accepting what was going on with me, including the possibility of cancer, even before I was actually diagnosed with it. I said to her, "Mother, I don't want you to pray that it's not cancer. I just want you and Dad to pray that I have the strength to accept whatever it is because it is already there." I'm sure they worried, but I am equally sure they prayed.

I felt strongly that if it were malignant, it was there now and an instant praying couldn't change a malignant tumor to a benign tumor. I just wanted to accept, to live with, and to cope with what was going on with me at that time. I have prayed and cried myself to sleep many nights. Instead of asking God that the outcome not be cancer, I prayed to *accept* the diagnosis and asked for guidance for the continuation of my life. I asked for a positive attitude and help to display this attitude. After God granted this to me, my prayers changed to "Thank you" and "Use me to help others to obtain this level of contentment which you have given me."

Chapter 5

From Recuperation to Reconstruction

I recuperated and returned to my rooming house with the community bathroom in Salem. Although I had no complications, I was wearing a temporary prosthesis which, I admit, was uncomfortable. My physician wanted me to wait until everything had healed before I had reconstructive surgery. The first morning there I woke up about two o'clock to go to the bathroom. I didn't know if I should put my prosthesis on just to go down the hallway. I didn't know if I was going to see someone, if the person would look at me. I sat on the side of my bed and debated with myself for an hour and a half: "Should I go? Should I not go?" I could hear my neighbors talking in their rooms, and I just didn't know what to do. Then all of a sudden, something came over me, and I said, "Look, you are alive. Get up, regardless of how you look, and go to that bathroom." I did not put on my prothesis. I went to the bathroom with just my gown, with my flat chest. From then on I went to the bathroom without my prosthesis, flat chested, just as I was.

Someone referred me to an eighty-year-old woman in Cambridge who made prostheses. When I walked in, she took one look at me and said, "Poor thing. Let me help you. Let me fit you with something that's more comfortable." (I still had a bale of cotton packed on me because I wanted to look like I did prior to going to the hospital.)

I was very pleased with that prosthesis, but my commitment to myself was to have reconstructive surgery. I wanted to look more like I had prior to surgery. As a fringe benefit of the reconstructive surgery, I would have a tummy tuck, and I was anxious to have these procedures completed.

But long before I had the reconstructive surgery, I had to make another adjustment. Seeing my private parts was strange. I was shocked because I had never seen my genital area. Looking straight down the front of my body with my breasts removed, I looked deformed, I thought, or different than what I was accustomed to seeing. With the breasts removed, my abdomen was up to my mid-chest. I asked the nurse, "Is this how you look? This is *this* high? Is this what I think it is here?"

She said, amusedly, "Yes, yes." There was no separation from breast to abdomen. So my body was new. It was definitely a strange body. I didn't even recognize myself. It was totally new for me. But that was okay because one of my salvations was to have the reconstructive surgery.

At the time I was in the hospital having my mastectomy in 1988 the National Cancer Institute issued a bulletin stating that all women having mastectomies, whether their lymph nodes are cancerous or not, should have some adjuvant therapy, secondary therapy to the primary treatment for breast cancer. Usually adjuvant therapy consists of chemotherapy, radiation, or pills. I immediately called my doctor. "Give me some of that adjuvant therapy! I need it!"

He said, "Well, Augusta, you don't need it because your lymph nodes are negative."

I said, "No, but the National Cancer Institute says whether your lymph nodes are negative or positive, you need that adjuvant therapy."

He said, "Well, you don't need it."

"I want it. Give it to me." So he wrote me a prescription for Tamoxifin and gave me verbal information regarding the drug. He indicated that it would increase my survival by only a small percentage. After the mastectomy, the doctors had told me that I had a ninety percent survival rate. I said, "Oh, no. I have a hundred percent. I can push that ninety to a hundred on my own."

When I was coming back from the hospital, I thought about the prescription I had demanded. I said, "I don't know if I want to take this pill." I would have had to take it for two years on a daily basis. Patients taking Tamoxifin had to be watched carefully and have blood work, too. I decided to go to Dana-Farber Cancer Institute in Boston to get a second opinion for adjuvant therapy. Of course, they got all my records from Sloan Kettering. The physician, Dr. Daniel Hayes, said, "You do not need adjuvant therapy." I asked him why, and he told me essentially the same thing as the doctor in New York had about negative lymph nodes and my tumor being less than a centimeter. Then he gave me a third reason: "We don't know the long-term effects of usage of the pill." That helped me to make the decision not to take the pill. He explained very well about weighing the risks and the benefits.

One of the things that I did, and I encourage others to do when they go for a second opinion, was to take a friend with me. Often I go in with my mind set to hear a specific diagnosis. Whatever else the doctor says goes right over me. When I left the doctor, my friend gave me information that I never heard because I was only concentrating on making a decision about whether or not I should take that pill.

In making any health care decision, I always weigh it, educate myself, and then respect the decision I make. I've had people ask if I don't need Tamoxifin. Emphatically, I say "No! I should not have it!" And I don't need to explain why I shouldn't have it. The point is, I made a decision, and I respect my own decision-making abilities.

As I healed and went to work everyday, I learned more about reconstructive surgery. About seven years prior to my mastectomy I had seen on television a doctor who did reconstructive surgery. I wrote his name and telephone number so that as I spoke for the American Cancer Society I could give this information to any person who needed it.

Now I found that doctor. He was shocked and amazed that I had seen him on television so long before and had kept his name and telephone number. We talked about the reconstructive surgery. I decided that I did not want to have a silicone prosthesis. I wanted to have my own tissue implanted because I felt there would be less chance of rejection by my body. The doctor agreed to perform the reconstructive surgery.

At that time I had a fairly large abdomen, so we decided to use my abdominal tissue. I asked about the chance of developing breast cancer again, and the doctor said the cancer would not recur because my breasts would now be abdominal rather than breast tissue. Regardless of how stupid a question sounds, I always think I should ask it anyway, because it is my life. I, not the doctor, have to live with it.

By the time I had the surgery, I looked as though I were six months pregnant! I gained more weight to ensure that I would have enough tissue for the reconstruction. After the reconstructive surgery, my stomach was very flat.

The doctor asked me what size did I wish my reconstructed breast to be. I knew I didn't want a double F, but I didn't know what I wanted. I said, "Just let me have enough so that I look kind of close to what I looked like before."

He said, "Okay. We can do that. You've got enough abdomen here."

In case I didn't, I had people all over the United States offering their abdomen tissue – black, tan, pink, all colors of abdomen offered to me!

The surgery took about ten hours. I was taken to the operating room about five o'clock that morning, and right away the anesthesiologist started the intravenous fluids and was ready to put me to sleep. I inquired, "Where is my doctor?"

"Oh, he's not here. He wants you to be sleeping so that when he comes in, he can start the procedure," the anesthesiologist said.

"Oh no," I said. You will not put me to sleep until my doctor walks into this room and says, 'Good morning, Augusta.'" I lay on the operating table for thirty minutes before the doctor arrived and inquired why I was not asleep. The staff informed him, and he walked over, "Good morning, Augusta."

I replied, then looked at the anesthesiologist and said, "You may put me to sleep." This clearly indicates taking control of what's happening to you. I have seen too many surgeries where the doctor went into the operating room and performed surgery on the wrong patient or body part!

The kind of reconstructive surgery I had is called a TRAM, for the trans rectus abdominal muscle. Surprisingly, the abdominal incision is not made in the abdominal area but from hip to hip. I call the incision "coast to coast." All of the fatty tissue, the abdominal tissue, was tunneled through the abdominal and chest wall, and the mastectomy incision reopened. Half of the tissue was placed on either side of my chest, and then the abdomen was pulled down to close the abdominal incision, and this was sewn so that it is flat. I still have a flat abdomen from that surgery. I had the nipples reconstructed at a later time here in Massachusetts.

I lost a lot of blood during the approximately ten-hour surgery. Worse, I had forgotten something very important. I guess I had so many tasks and worries on my mind it just never dawned on me to have my blood taken from me and waiting for me in case I needed it. My blood count had dropped severely. The morning after the surgery, the doctors said, "We're going to have to give you a blood transfusion."

Because of my fear of contracting blood-borne pathogens such as AIDS or hepatitis, I replied, "No, I do not want a blood transfusion."

My doctor argued, "You need that blood because of the surgery. You're going to interfere with the surgical process." Now here I had a doctor not taking into consideration my needs and wants. He just wanted to give me that blood transfusion because it's a quick solution.

I said, "Look, why don't you get the nutritionist in to help me select foods that are high in iron? Give me some iron tablets;

put me on complete bed rest." I had my way. You can probably guess what happened. About two or three days after that my hematocrit started creeping up. I was put in a Trendelenburg position – where the head of the bed is lower than the foot so that the blood goes to the head.

Two or three days after the surgery, my hematocrit started climbing, so the doctor said, "We're going to let you out of bed today." I got out of bed and stabilized myself and proceeded to go in the bathroom. I saw stars, moons, and everything else because of the position I had been in before. I was holding on to the wall as I was walking to the bathroom. And I got to the bathroom with a nurse's assistant's help.

"Oh, I'm passing out. Call the nurse! Get me to the bed! Get me some oxygen!" She called out for the nurse who came in and found me with my head down.

The staff followed my orders. After a couple of minutes, I felt fine, but I had to stay on bed rest for another day. My blood count slowly but steadily climbed until it was safe for me to be discharged.

I recall praying specifically for my blood count to return to normal. The first night I dreamed that little red blood cells shaped like M & M candy with very skinny arms and legs floated down a fall, rushing to deliver red blood cells to me. In spite of the medical staff's insistence that I receive blood and prediction of a negative outcome for me if I continued to refuse the blood, I knew that someone greater than the physicians and medical staff was watching over me. I had consutlted with my heavenly father, and I knew everything was going to be all right for me.

Again my cousin, Jim Buckley, came to pick me up from the hospital. I stayed with him a couple of days before I went to Louisiana. Enroute from the hospital to his house, I saw a manicure place. I stayed in the house the first day and rested. The next day he went to work, and I decided I would go out – after all this surgery – and find that manicurist because I still wanted to feel good about myself, to look good, to feel better. I had obviously misjudged the distance. I started walking; I got tired and decided to wait for a cab. With not one cab in sight, I stopped and had lunch and then proceeded on foot. I found the place and had my nails manicured.

In the meantime, my cousin had called his house and not received an answer. Of course, he didn't know what had happened to me. He called the hospitals to see if I had been readmitted. Learning that I had not, he dashed home only to see me strolling along with beautifully manicured nails. "You are too, too, too much!" was his only comment.

The Rev. Perry and Dorothy Wesley Hicks, my father and stepmother, 1992

I went to Louisiana again to recuperate. My mom was my nurse. I had a list of foods that were high in iron. I had iron snacks, iron in the morning, noon, and night. Before I left Louisiana, my blood count was normal. I had gone to the doctor there in Ruston to check out a slight complication with my incision which had opened. I asked the staff to check my hematocrit because I wanted to know my progress. I recuperated and returned to Boston and started to work.

After the reconstructive surgery I participated in a video called *"A Sense of Balance"* which explains the different types of reconstructive surgery. The information is quite extensive for women who are contemplating this procedure.

Although a breast can never be reconstructed as the original piece of art it was, the technology of plastic surgery has dramatically improved over the last thirty years. Initially I was just pleased to have a mound there, happy I was not flat chested. I can remember my mother saying to me when I told her about the nipple construction, "Why do you want to have that done? There's nothing wrong with you now. You've had enough surgery. Why don't you just let well enough do?" I know that was good for my mother, but I have to live with my body image for the rest of my life. I have to be happy. I have to be pleased. I have to be comfortable with what's going on with me. So I elected to have a nipple reconstruction.

Again I was reminded that we black people are blessed with variations of skin colors on our bodies. The plastic surgeon was able to transfer some of the dark tissues from the ends of my abdominal incision to the breasts and construct the nipples. They look like "normal nipples." Sometimes doctors tattoo a nipple. However, if possible, I like to use my own body parts so that I have less of a reaction to whatever is used. The nipple reconstruction was the end, a kind of culmination for me in this whole saga of breast cancer.

Chapter 6

The Lymphedema Nightmare

What I have labeled in my file as the "lymphedema nightmare" was the next step of this process. Excessive fluid or swelling in the arms which can occur after a mastectomy is called *lymphedema*. It is caused by injury or trauma to the lymphatic system. The lymph nodes are often removed because the lymph system is the vehicle by which fluid is circulated throughout the body and certain cancer cells can travel and be deposited at different sites in the body. This is why it is extremely important to feel under the armpits when examining the breasts. What women should know is they cannot feel the lymph nodes if there's no disease. Only if there is a disease will there be swelling or lumpiness. Many times when people have radiation to the breast, the lymph nodes are damaged from the radiation.

My lymphedema "nightmare" occurred about two and a half years after I had the mastectomy. Sometimes it will occur immediately after a mastectomy, and sometimes it is delayed fifteen or twenty years. Other times it may never occur. The manner of the onset of lymphedema varies. Some women report that they think they did something to aggravate it, something minimal initially. One woman indicated that she was out on a picnic and was bitten by an insect when her arm started swelling. The arm of a woman who has had a mastectomy and lymph nodes removed will often swell like a balloon if it is subjected to something traumatic such as an insect bite or an injury.

I first noticed my lymphedema one day when I saw on my arm the indentations of the bangles I had worn. When I examined my arm, I noticed the fluid. One visit to the oncologist at the hospital where I was working convinced me to get a pump to reduce swelling although I had done little research on it. I got one from the durable medical equipment company.

I had no idea how to use the pump nor at what setting it should be used, and at the time I picked it up, there was no one there to explain its usage. So I called the doctor. Since it was Friday of a holiday weekend, he was on his way out of town. Someone in the breast clinic in Boston refused to help because I was not a patient there. Not to be deterred, I said, "I need you to tell me something today. This is Friday, and my doctor's away, and I have this pump, and I don't know how to use it or anything about it." I was given an appointment to come in the next Monday. In the meantime I remembered a physical therapist from my support group who had had a mastectomy, and I contacted her. She invited me to come down to the hospital where she was working and showed me how to use the pump.

This was what I call a generic pump. The sleeve constricted and relaxed my arm. I knew I was to use it every day, which I did. But I didn't see a lot of results, so I went to get a second opinion from another doctor. He gave me information about a better pump as well as where to get one.

A young woman at the medical supply store brought the pump out to me and gave me instructions to use it. I had to ask her to measure my arm so that I could see the difference in the size and thus know the outcome. This woman was not a medical person, nor did she have lymphedema. I felt that I was in a better position to explain the use of that pump and to share some personal findings. I called the company in Pennsylvania and shared my experiences and thoughts about the pump with them. They asked me to fly out to an interview for a job as a consultant with the company. I did, and I was hired. Now when women in the New England area need the bio-compression pump, I take it out and instruct them in its usage.

A woman with the most severe lymphedema I had ever seen came to my support group. Hers was so severe! The lymphedema ran the length of her arm. Her neck and her chest were also affected. Her affected arm looked five, ten times the size of her other arm! She had a sling on her arm because it was so swollen and heavy.

I told her about the pump. Initially her doctor refused to order it for her. Perhaps he didn't know about this new and improved pump. I asked her if she would like me to speak with her doctor, and she agreed. I called him and educated him about the pump, which he ordered for her. When I carried it to her, I had her lie down, put her feet on the bed, and relax. I moved the telephone close to her and told her that if she needed anything, I would get it for her so that she could have it right where she could reach it with her other arm. She looked at me and said, "Oh, I wish you could come every day and help me."

I did visit her periodically, and I would see her at the support meeting. The first time I saw her after I delivered the pump, she looked like a different person. The swelling had decreased significantly. She rarely spoke at the meetings, but during one meeting we had a company representative talk about a compression pump. She raised her hand and said, "I just want to share one thing with you: the pump you have here, I don't know anything about. But that pump that Augusta has works! I know about that pump. Look at my arm!"

I went several times to see Dr. Sumner Slavin, a plastic surgeon who is an expert on lymphedema. He conducted a lymphoscintrogram, a procedure in which a dye is injected in the hand to trace the lymphatic system of the arm to see where the blockage occurs. Although I had never heard of it, it made sense to me. The doctor said, "Let's check first to see if you're a candidate for that pump because if you're all blocked up, you will not benefit from the pump." But my insurance would not approve a visit to him because he was not in the network. Consequently, I had to pay out of my pocket to go see the doctor as well as pay for my insurance. I had my insurance from another job, but because of the existing health condition I was not covered on my current job until after I had been there a year.

I didn't then, and don't now, think it was fair to pay several hundred dollars every month for my insurance premium and then pay out of my pocket for my doctor's visits. I decided to call the insurance company one more time and request authorization to see Dr. Slavin. This was my third contact with the insurance company. My private doctor had written two letters to them requesting that I see Dr. Slavin. The answer was "no" both times. Of course, I asked why and was told that there were physicians in this particular network who treated lymphedema.

I asked the insurance company for a referral and received the names of five physicians who treated lymphedema. When I tried to follow up on the referrals, I found that one had retired, one did not treat lymphedema, and two had disconnected telephones. Finally, I made an appointment with the fifth one, only to have him say to me, "You have lymphedema." He suggested that I elevate my arm, adding that there was nothing that he could do. I smiled and left his office never to return.

At this point I was more determined than ever that my insurance company allow me to see Dr. Slavin. I called the insurance company and gave them an ultimatum: "Either you allow me to see Dr. Slavin, or I will call the television stations, newspapers, and my lawyer because you are blocking my access to quality care. I will give you one week to make the decision." For about half an hour we talked about the referrals they had made and how they prevented me from seeing a qualified plastic surgeon who specialized in lymphedema. After a week I called them and learned that they had not changed their mind. I would not be allowed to see the doctor of my choice. So I thanked them and proceeded to follow up with my promise.

I called Liz Walker, news anchor of WBZ television in Boston and told her my story and requested help. She said she would come out to interview me and report it in a news story. She also suggested that she interview Dr. Slavin. He initially agreed to the interview, but later declined because of hospital policy regarding interviews in such situations. Liz contacted the hospital because of Dr. Slavin's expertise and interest, then she called the insurance company and left a simple message: "This is Liz Walker of Channel 4, and I am calling regarding Augusta Gale."

The next day I received a call from my insurance company stating, "We want to inform you of some changes here. We're going to allow you to see Dr. Slavin." When I called to make the appointment with Dr. Slavin, the nurse asked me what I did to cause the president of the insurance company himself to call to authorize my visit. My advocacy prevailed.

Dr. Slavin provided information all survivors of mastectomies should have. It is imperative that women be taught how to care for the arm on the side where the surgery was performed. No blood pressure should be taken in the arm because of the possibility of further damaging the lymphatic system. When cooking women should be very careful to protect the arm. Mittens should be used to remove items from the stove. Extreme variations of temperature are not good, nor is lifting heavy objects. Women who carry purses that weigh a ton should switch to lighter purses if they have had a bilateral mastectomy. Those having had a unilateral mastectomy should use the opposite side than that on which surgery was performed. I practically live with an antibiotic ointment, such as Bacitracin, that can be bought over the counter, so that I can apply it if I notice the slightest injury on the lymphedemic side. Applying the ointment can help prevent infection, soreness, and discoloration. I notice that when I get something as small as a paper cut healing requires several days, and the spot is sore during that time.

Many doctors deny that lymphedema exists. Others say that due to the improvement in the technology and drugs connected with the mastectomy, we rarely see it. However, women should be aware of the fact that lymphedema can be a complication of mastectomy; many of us must battle this condition.

I have met women across the country with lymphedema. I see big swollen arms everyday. Sometimes I mention the swollen arms and talk about lymphedema just to support a woman who has it. Depending on the severity of the case, I suggest that women use the biocompression pump after consulting their doctor. Sometimes doctors will say, "Just elevate your arms; there's nothing we can do about it." Wrong! Elevating the arms brings only temporary relief. There are choices in treatment for lymphedema — biocompression pumps, manual lymph drainage (MLD), massage therapy, and excercises.

My parents and I at the dedication of the Jettie Hicks Hoard Day Care Center, Evanston, Illinois, 1983. Aunt Jettie is my father's youngest sister.

Chapter 7

Saying Cancer Out Loud

There is more information about health care after mastectomy than was available thirty years ago. I follow the instructions rigidly. Two to three times a week, for five-minute sessions, the chest muscles must be exercised. I use a baton which I raise above my head and behind my neck. A broomstick would work equally well. This also exercises my fingers. Because of the lymphedema, I must open my fist slowly about one hundred times while having my arm elevated. This exercise is important, even if a woman does not have visible lymphedema. The exercise is particularly important for the woman who has had lymph node dissection.

I am very careful about what I eat. I always watch my fat intake. I have eliminated almost all fried food. I have reduced the amount of red meat in my diet, preferring fish and chicken.

I always get eight to ten hours of sleep because the body needs time to restore itself. If I did not need the rest, I think I would wake up. I always listen to my body. It tells me when I have had enough rest.

More than ever, since my mastectomy, I am reminded how much breasts are associated with sex and intimacy. Reminders are everywhere: in magazines and newspapers and on television where women with large breasts wear low cut dresses. Society is trained to see large breasts as attractive. I was quite concerned about how I looked and what people would think of me without my large breasts. We all want to appear "normal," even if we've lost our breasts. Reconstructive surgery was one of my salvations.

Of course, women are concerned with the effect of mastectomies on their sex lives. I have the good fortune to have a mature and sensitive companion who admired my FF breast size when he met me yet who assured me that it has no effect upon our relationship.

From time to time women in my breast cancer support group share their experiences. One of them, a twenty-five-year-old, single woman who had had a lumpectomy, was anxious to know just when she should tell a man she had recently met, "By the way, I am 3/4s silicone." The answer from the group was unanimous: "You tell him whenever you are comfortable."

Breast cancer activists Pam Ferguson, Bernadette Winiker and I. Photograph taken by health researcher Lise Beane at the Massachusetts Breast Cancer Coalition Rally in Boston, 1990.

Another woman in the group said she and her husband discussed new areas for foreplay which proved to be exciting for them. Some women specifically suggested other erogenous zones, such as behind the ears, the inner aspect of the thighs, and the buttocks.

Although it is sometimes very hard to do, I encourage men to talk with their spouses or partners, tell the women they want to be supportive but are having trouble expressing their feelings. I think women would appreciate hearing the words. Somebody has to open the door; then both the man and the woman can talk about their feelings. After all, sexual intimacy is a shared experience, and one of the thrills could come from working as closely as possible as a team.

One of the responses which put me at my greatest ease was hearing, "You know, there's a little something wrong with all of us." In theory, all of us probably know this and agree it is true. But when we ourselves are faced with that which is not "normal," we sometimes need to be reminded that no one is perfect. The woman fortunate enough to have a partner state the not always obvious is blessed. The woman able to remember it for herself may be more blessed.

Although I occasionally hear of some totally insensitive responses to a woman's mastectomy, the more likely experience of a woman in a warm and loving relationship is her lover's or her husband's concern about her health and well-being. I have talked to men who want to support their partners, but don't know what to do. There are local support groups in some places for men who are having problems dealing with their partners' mastectomies or simply feeling that they would like guidance in being more supportive. Some doctors or the local American Cancer Society may have information concerning such groups.

To those who have difficulty just saying the word "cancer" to me, I say "speak;" Say the word anytime. People do not have to worry about my reaction. They do not have to skirt the issue. As a survivor, I play an important role because people will base their reactions and interactions with me on my behavior. If I am comfortable, if I speak the word "cancer," talk out loud about it, then people will follow suit.

One of my most memorable encounters in this area happened after the publication of my *Ebony* article on breast cancer. I was telling one of my friends in Connecticut about the article and how I coped with the cancer. She looked at me and said, "Is your name on the article?"

And I said, "Of course. Sure. It's about me."

Horror-struck, she said, "But everybody is going to know that you're...." She could not finish the sentence.

I said, "I don't care! I'm alive. This can be a learning experience for other women."

This is my proof that many people are still in the closet about cancer. They just don't want to speak out or talk about it. It's still something they want to avoid mentioning as if it has not happened. I recall an incident that influenced me and really helped me to make the decision to go public with that article. After I came from the hospital, one of the women living in the rooming house with me visited me and asked, "What do they do when they do a mastectomy?" Now, this is an intelligent, educated woman. She said, "Do they just cut the breast on the side, take everything out, and sew it back up?" I showed her what a mastectomy looked like, showed her my flat chest. She saw that all of the breast tissue was removed. All along I was thinking, if this woman does not understand, and she's an intelligent, well-educated person, what about all the rest without education and no exposure? What do they think? They may indeed think horrible things. No wonder.

This woman was far from being in a class by herself. This incident provoked a variety of thoughts. I've heard bright people say, "Oh, if I had cancer of the breast, or even if I have gangrene of the leg, just let it stay there." Or, "I came in the world like this, and I want to go out as a whole person. I want to go out like I came in." They fail to consider that this is not the way they came into the world and often the abnormal can be treated or eliminated. Since I hear such comments across the country, I am very disturbed. We still need a lot of education on health matters. This is my only answer for individuals not seeking health care: "Why?" I always try to get to the root of inaction because it can be deadly.

Chapter 8
Doctors and Pedestals

I don't know why so many patients feel that doctors are on pedestals, that whatever they say is gospel, that they should not be challenged or even hear the patients' point of view. But it is necessary for us patients to speak. We speak and collaborate with the doctors so that we can be empowered, so that we can be advocates, so that we can be assertive, so that others can learn and perhaps act.

We live in a society that oftentimes tells us what to do, when, where and why, but almost never **how** to do a particular thing. But we can become empowered to advocate for ourselves. I use the term "advocate" to speak to or address the issues concerning us personally.

Why should one advocate? Well, if you experience a major illness or hospitalization there are so many others controlling your outcome. You can compare going into a health care facility in some ways to going into a correctional institution. In both cases rehabilitation is the goal in order to return the individual back to society better than he or she was upon leaving it. Sometimes this is not true. We become a statistic rather than an informed consumer or an empowered person to speak up for ourselves. Upon entering both of these facilities your clothes are removed, you are given a gown or uniform, an identification bracelet or a series of identification numbers. There is a scheduled time for meals, usually eight, twelve and five. And if you want to eat at nine, one and six? No such luck. There are designated visiting hours, sleep and awakening times, so you must be able to speak and act on your behalf, or you just might remain a number or statistic. As much as is possible, a person must speak for her or himself, be an advocate.

I learn everything I can about what is going on with me. My being a nurse is no reason for any lay person to say she or he cannot be informed. There is no excuse. But first it is necessary to become empowered. And how does one become empowered? Through knowledge. This knowledge may be obtained by reading, doing research, attending seminars, workshops or lectures, going to the library, various hospital resource centers. A lot of these places and activities are free. Official agencies or organizations set up for specific diseases such as the American Cancer Society, the Heart Association and the Diabetes Association have free brochures and helpful information. The public should take advantage of these opportunities.

One of the best sources about your health is your medical records. Read your medical records. I was recently hospitalized and wanted to obtain my medical record upon discharge. The procedure was simple. Two hours before discharge the medical records department sent my progress notes and a release form for me to sign. The doctor's notes were given to me upon discharge. For the x-ray report and blood work I was required to go to the medical records department to sign a release form, and within two weeks the reports were mailed to me.

You have the right to read and obtain your medical record in its entirety. To do this first contact your doctor or medical institution to learn the procedure for obtaining such records. The protocol may vary from one doctor or institution to another. Doctors and institutions usually have ten business days to inform a client whether or not he or she can obtain the record, and are required by some state laws to do so within thirty days. Hospitals may charge the client the actual photocopying cost, but no other fees. In making a written request to obtain a medical record, it's a good idea to keep a copy of the request. Most doctors and institutions readily comply. However, if a request is denied, ask the hospital or doctor to state in writing why access to the record is not allowed and how to appeal this decision.

You have several alternatives if your request is denied. You may want to ask a friendly doctor to contact the provider to send him or her your record and then share the record with you. There is an American Medical Association provision requiring your treating doctor to transfer your records to your new doctor at your request. If pushed, you may threaten to sue or actually sue.

If you're wondering why you should get your records, consider these reasons:

1. You cannot be an effective member of your health team if you are not privy to the game plan.
2. You may want to seek a second opinion or change primary care providers after you read your medical record.
3. You want to ensure that the information in the record about you is accurate.
4. You want access to a base of information that may be helpful in dealing with potential long-term consequences of catastrophic illness.

If after obtaining your medical record and you have additional requests or concerns, then I strongly suggest going to the top, the head of the organization or institution, to get results.

A few words of caution: decide for yourself. Sometimes when you discuss or reveal your course of action, family and friends may attempt to deter you. Despite how well meaning they are, you should decide for yourself. Others may have a tendency to make you doubt yourself.

Becoming a partner with your doctor is the other aspect of empowerment. How do you become a partner with your doctor?

1. Speak frankly to your doctor. He or she cannot read your mind although some may appear to think they can.
2. Bring a family member to assist you to listen to what the doctor is presenting to you.
3. Jot down questions before your visit and take them with you. Or you may want to write all your questions

and concerns in a letter to your doctor prior to the visit so he or she will have had an opportunity to research your concerns. How many times have you left the doctor's office and forgot to ask him or her something?

4. Don't present yourself as a disease, but rather as a person with a disease. Tell your doctor about yourself: whether you are married, single, have children, grandchildren, etc.

5. Ask for permission to tape the conversation so that you can replay it to make sure you understood what the doctor said to you.

6. Ask for definitions of puzzling medical words and terms so that you understand the information the doctor is presenting to you.

7. Find out where, and when, to call if you have a problem, as well as how to make contact in emergency situations.

8. Before you leave the doctor's office, you should understand your diagnosis and treatment plan. Ask the doctor to put it in writing.

9. Let the doctor know your expectations from him or her, and that you would like to be included in all aspects of your care.

10. Finally, if you can't communicate with your doctor, then maybe you need another doctor. Remember, you do not own stock with any particular doctor, but you do own 100% stock in yourself.

Chapter 9
The Power of
Self-Advocacy

After my reconstructive surgery I returned to Boston with renewed energy. I began my advocacy-for-empowerment speeches and programs for other women. Somehow it seemed that all of my experiences had led me to this point. My involvement with breast cancer and the health care system confirmed what I have known for a very long time: people should know that they have options. They can have a second opinion or if needed, a third opinion. And they should assess and evaluate what the first physician told them. They need to find out on what they agree and on what they disagree. A third opinion may be needed to clear up the differences. It is extremely important to get more than one opinion. Plans for the future should be made only after listening carefully to all of the possibilities.

From each medical encounter I have learned valuable information about how to manage my health care to make it work for me. Keeping my medical files is one such practice which has turned out to be quite valuable. Whenever I go to the doctor, I request a copy of every report for my personal medical files. In his or her report I can see what the doctor has written about me. Then I can monitor my progress or lack of it. I have all my blood work reports because I want to monitor my blood's condition. When I go into a doctor's office, I am told many times, "Oh, this is within normal range." But if I'm in the high part of the range, or nearly outside of the range, I want to know why. I want to be closer to the lower part of the normal. So, I keep my own records. And if I have a report and I go in next time and it's higher, I want to be told why this report is higher than it was three months ago. What's going on? Or is there something going on? Explain to me. I have a copy of all my x-ray reports, all my laboratory reports, and the doctors' reports.

Once I saw a report that was totally different from the information I had given the doctor. It was not what I had said; it was not what had happened, and I advised the doctor accordingly. Eventually I was proved correct. I always get my report and read it.

I do not hesitate to collaborate with friends in the medical profession. I talk with others so that when I meet with my physician, I can collaborate with him or her and I can talk with the doctor and understand what he or she is saying.

It is important to learn where to call and the times to call in case there is a problem. I try to make sure I understand beforehand the procedure for making contact with the doctor in emergency situations.

Despite my being a nurse, physicians sometimes use unfamiliar terms. However, I won't sit through a conversation without knowing what the physician is saying, shaking my head as if I know. The doctors can understandably run through this information if I don't stop them. But if I question them, they listen to me. But some will not explain in detail on their own. I, the patient, have to make an effort. It's my health. I have to let the doctors know right away who I am, what I am about, what I expect.

I've even gone so far as to send a letter to the doctor *prior* to my visit to let him or her know my interests. I know that most of us human beings, including doctors, don't want to admit that we don't know. Rather than get there and ask the doctor something he or she doesn't know during my office visit, and have him or her give me misinformation or incomplete information, I prefer forewarning the person about what I want to know so that he or she can have an answer for me. Any patient can do the same and thus advocate for herself.

Sometimes it is extremely frustrating, if not impossible, to communicate with a doctor. If that is the case, I conclude that it is probably time to find another doctor, someone with whom I can become a partner in my health care.

Over the years, people have occasionally been subjected to great harm in the name of medical treatment. Of course, sometimes people willingly took risks because they were grasping for straws. At other times some of the drugs were in the experimental stage when patients received them, and the patients were not given all the necessary information they needed to make decisions to use them. Surely if women are told the harmful or even possibly harmful effects of a drug, they will not accept that drug. But when they're in a desperate situation, and if they hear of something that might help, they're going to try it. Thalidomide, which caused abnormalities in fetuses, was one of the most diastrous such cases. The feeding of radiation-contaminated oatmeal to children in a Massachusetts shelter without the awareness of the children or their parents in the 1950s was another tragic procedure reported in the news media in 1995. One of the saddest revelations for me as a health care professional and a black person was the Tuskegee Syphilis Experiment in which treatment was deliberately withheld from a group of black men in Alabama during the 1930s as part of a medical experiment.

One way to avoid medical disasters or at least reduce our exposure to them is to be an advocate. We can start with something very simple. We do not start with advocating or making decisions for life-threatening conditions. For example, when I call a department store, and I only want to know the closing time, I am invariably answered with, "Hold on."

"No! I only want to know what time your store closes."

"8:00 p.m." That's it. Why make me hold the phone for fifteen minutes?

And then I can say, "Whoa." I build up confidence. I can control. I am in control. Then I move into more complex situations.

I must admit that all of my responses have not come from the disease, but the cancer has made me more aware of my own potential power. My responses to the complexities of my own breast cancer have been so liberating for me that I hope my sharing some of them will be useful to others. I developed my assertiveness and got more of what I wanted in other ways not strictly related to my experience with breast cancer, all of which probably reinforced my confidence, in less threatening situations.

When I was living in Salem, Sears and Roebuck delivered a washing machine to me. They installed it, and they wanted their payment immediately. I had mistakenly left my purse in Swampscott, a neighboring town, because I was moving. The workmen said, "We're gonna go to Lynn," which is the next little town over from Salem.

I said, "Okay, why don't you stop by, just swing over in Swampscott, and let me get my checkbook, which is in my purse, and I'll pay you."

One of the men said yes. Apparently he went down and talked with his partner who exclaimed, "Oh, no! We're not doing that! We'll take this machine out of here!"

I said fine. They took it out. I got on the phone and asked for the Information number for the Sears Tower in Chicago. Although I know both Sears and Roebuck died many years ago I dialed the number and said, "May I speak with Mr. Sears and Roebuck?"

The person answering said, "That's impossible, but we can let you speak with somebody who can help you." And I told them my problem, what the deliverymen had done.

They replied, "Don't worry. Somebody from the Northshore Shopping Center Sears and Roebuck will call you today."

Indeed, someone called me that night, apologizing, and wanting to know when I wanted my washing machine delivered. "We will deliver it at any time that is convenient to you," they offered. And the time that was convenient for me was a Sunday evening after I'd gone to church and I would be relaxing, waiting to go to work the next morning. They brought my machine out Sunday evening and installed it. "And for you, Ms. Gale, there will be no delivery charge."

There was another incident where I went to the top to advocate for myself. While I was in the hospital the postal service thoroughly mishandled my mail. When I came back from the hospital after the mastectomy, I found mail over here and over there, under pieces of furniture, and strewn about in the vestibule of the rooming house. I said, "My God! What is going on?" Then they told me they could not hold the mail for one person in a rooming house unless the roomer gave an apartment or room number. Otherwise it would require holding everybody's mail, but nobody from the post office informed me of that when I went in earlier and asked them to hold my mail. So I said okay.

I went to let the post office know I was out of the hospital, but they held my mail instead of delivering it. So, I was sitting there waiting. It was around my birthday when I usually get three or four dozen cards, but I hadn't gotten a single one! I said, "Something is wrong." I thought, "Oh, maybe it's because I was sick and people sent me cards and they said that's enough for you." I was expecting money from insurance companies and other important mail. I made long distance calls to track some of them down. I went to the local post office and asked the postmaster about it. I told him what had happened, that I had not received mail that I was expecting and had made long distance calls trying to find out what was happening. He said that he would reimburse me for the long distance calls if I would bring the receipts, which I did.

A short time later the post office made a big error. That was it. I wrote the Postmaster General in Washington, D. C., and there was an investigation at the Salem Post Office. I understand that there were some changes made at the post office. One day after I moved to Swampscott, I was coming out of my building, and the postman saw me. He said, pointing to the building where I lived, "Do you live in the east building?"

Reluctantly, I said, "Yes."

He said, "Are you Augusta Gale?"

Again, I reluctantly said, "yes."

He said, "My name is Sammy. I'm your mailman. If you have any problems, you call Sammy, and I'll take care of your mail for you."

In the meantime, the postmaster from Woburn, the central post office here in New England where the mail is sent and then dispersed, called to ask me if I received my mail okay or if I had any problems. So, do you think the post office in Swampscott knew Augusta Gale? I found out they did when I received a letter in response to the *Ebony* article. Its address simply said, "Augusta Gale, Black Nurse, Salem, Massachusetts."

Chapter 10

God Will Take Care of Me But What Do I Do?

Much of my advocacy is directed at African Americans because we are so often overlooked, abused, used, and misused. But I am wise enough to know that we cannot – or at least should not – always blame others for our problems. About fifteen years prior to my breast cancer diagnosis I was doing public education, speaking as a volunteer for the American Cancer Society. Little did I know at that time just how valuable such information would be for me one day. I spoke at various churches. I tried to do an outreach for African Americans, but I stopped because black people would rarely come back to church on Thursday night for a health discussion. It always distressed me that when I would go to white areas, the places would be packed. I wondered, "Why can't black people come out and get some of this information?" So I tapped into the existing church program. Although people would not come back during the week to hear someone talk about health, they would remain an additional half hour after the regular Sunday morning service to hear about preventive health care. I would speak with the minister, get his approval, let him buy into what I was talking about, and win him over. Then he would promote the program for me.

One Sunday I went to a large church in Chicago. There were about three hundred people there. The minister actually locked the doors of the church, and he said, "No one will leave until you hear this young lady speak. She' s gonna tell us something that all of us need to hear." This was general information about cancer, just to get people thinking about their health and empowering them, giving them some knowledge so that they could advocate for themselves. That's how I got started going to black churches, tapping into existing programs, trying to reach people, which proved very effective.

I have used that technique and that method in Illinois, Kentucky, and Massachusetts. I also joined the parishioners for service enabling me to hear the Word and anchor my faith.

When I go to various meetings which are attended by very few black people, I often hear someone say, "We need to reach black people." I hear that said frequently, but I don't see people sending us specifics to reach the black people. I guess it's an expression that people want to say. Malcolm X referred to such incidents when he spoke of people becoming involved in activities just for status, not with their hearts and souls in the effort.

Clearly there is a need for more aggressive health care. One possible explanation for personal inaction or delay in seeking medical care may lie in a health belief model developed in the early 1950s. It is not complete, but it's about the best explanation I know for why people don't seek medical attention. A summary goes something like this: If people feel that they are not susceptible to a disease, they will not seek help. In trying to analyze the problem, I realized that most of the pamphlets on breast cancer from the American Cancer Society had white people on them. It is possible that many black people would just look at the pictures and say, "Well, this doesn't affect me; it's a disease of white people. I don't see any black people's pictures on here." I pointed this out at many community meetings, and now there are black people's pictures on some of the brochures for breast cancer. Surely some have seen the connection between it and themselves.

The other part of the health belief model states that in order for people to seek health care, they must know that there is treatment for the disease. They must also know that the treatment is far better than the disease itself. They must believe that the disease would have serious effects on their lives if they should contract it. I try to incorporate some of these health belief models when instituting a program that will assist black people in seeking health care. I plan occasions to talk to one person at a time. I meet people in areas with which they are familiar – in the church and community.

I always wanted to help people, and I get feedback. It's like a loop: I give and I receive. Good things come back to me. Being a nurse diagnosed with breast cancer has provided countless opportunities for sharing what I know.

There was a time when I would say to myself, "Why can't black people call me and get this kind of information the same as some white people do?" Fortunately I have seen a turn, and more black people are calling me, asking my advice on their health issues, and I'm really excited about that.

My father was hospitalized and my stepmother called upon me to help. I was not pleased with the lack of respect or dignity shown my blind, slightly deaf father. He was given medication but not always aware of why he received it. I asked if I could assist in setting up his care plan. I first had his chart flagged to indicate that he was blind and hard of hearing; everything should be explained to him so that my father could cooperate and participate in his care. I spoke with the doctor, and we both determined at the same time that my father was reacting to a medication he had been given for a fungus infection. The medication was discontinued and he recovered and was discharged.

I played a different yet helpful role when my stepmother had heart surgery. I was unable to be with her, but I spoke with her daily in the coronary care unit. She was transferred from the local community hospital to a larger facility which performed bypass cardiac surgery. I flew to Sherveport, Louisiana to be with her after her surgery. Upon my arrival, my mother, in the Intensive Cardiac Care Unit, was so happy to see me that the nurses allowed me to go in and say hello at midnight. I spent the night at the family center at the hospital, and the next day my mom was transferred to a cardiac floor where I was allowed to stay in the room with her.

I assisted her with her breathing exercises, her physical therapy and meal selection and collaborated with the doctor. The moment she asked for her "hair" (wig) in the drawer and put on her makeup and gown, I knew her spirits had been lifted and she was on the way to recovery. The doctor came to visit and said they had never had a patient recover so quickly. Within a couple of days my mom was discharged without complications. She said she remembered my story in the *Ebony* magazine about how I felt good about myself so she applied the same concept during her illness.

My eighty-something year old Aunt Mattie Hicks in Chicago has certainly used my empowerment strategies to her advantage. She shared with me that her doctor had prescribed a new medicine for her. She asked if he had any samples. "Oh, yes, I think I do have some samples," the doctor replied and gave some to her. Aunt Mattie told me, "See, I am learning from you how to speak up."

I assisted my uncle, David Hasson, in California by teaching him about his medication and daily exercises, and prepared food which stimulated his appetite. We spent a lot of time reminiscing and eating together during his last days. His wife, Aunt Lorene, said the nursing "was all done with loving care."

On one of my visits to my parents in Louisiana a friend approached me and said, "I saw your article in the *Ebony* magazine, and I would like you to talk to a friend of mine who had a mastectomy." I went to see the woman who had had the surgery, and she said, "Everyone is telling me God will take care of me, and to move on with my life, but no one is telling me what to do. Here I am. What do I do?"

I looked at her and made a quick assessment. It was about two o'clock in the afternoon. I said, "Do you keep your pj's on all day, with your hair in rollers, and no makeup on?"

"No, I am a beautician," she said. I suggested that she call the American Cancer Society for a temporary prothesis so she would be balanced with one breast removed, take off the pj's and get dressed, style her hair and get back to work as soon as possible.

Two or three days later I received a call from this person, inviting me to revisit her. I went, and I hardly recognized her as the same person I had seen a few days before. She looked like a totally different person. Her hair was beautifully styled. She had followed through and contacted the American Cancer Society for a temporary prosthesis. She was fully dressed, and she indicated that she was ready to return to work, and did so.

A young woman from Chicago had met a mutual friend, and the friend suggested she call me. I sent her information on breast cancer and its treatment and called to support her in the hospital, and upon her return home. Her husband told me how happy she was and how positive she became about her illness after she spoke with me. I could hear a much more certain note in her voice.

Mother's Day March, sponsored by the Women's Community Cancer Project of Cambridge, Massachusetts. I am near the center wearing a white corsage and carrying a sign that says, "My corsage is in memory of my mother who died of breast cancer." Boston, 1991.

Later on, she called me to tell me she had a recurrence of cancer after completing chemotherapy and returning to work. She was more assertive than ever and determined that she would be a part of her care. She informed me that her doctor was going to give her another course of chemotherapy in spite of her insistence that she did not want it, but wanted a bone marrow transplant and would not settle for any other form of treatment. I suggested that she educate herself regarding this treatment and continue to advocate for herself.

Several of the parishioners from my church consider me as their personal health consultant. I've accompanied them to the doctor's office to help them understand the medical information and how to work through the health care system.

As a "Reach to Recovery" volunteer, I have met many women individually who have been diagnosed with breast cancer and have had a mastectomy or a lumpectomy. The "Reach to Recovery" program, sponsored by the American Cancer Society is an effective way to reach women shortly after a mastectomy or lumpectomy. The volunteer has been trained to speak with women and to support them because she has had the same diagnosis and can identify and assist with the emotional recovery, after she herself has recovered from breast cancer treatment.

Chapter 11

Getting the Message to the People

Somehow we need to get out of this learned helplessness mode that many of us have fallen into. Leaders and responsible ministers in the church should seek out people who have the knowledge and bring them to their parishioners and help in the educating process. We have many black leaders who are in positions to make this happen by setting the format for health education.

We just need to get out and educate our black people. I feel that we are not getting the kind of care that we should have. We have to do like the missionaries did years ago: get out and go where the people are. We have to go in the community. Go door-to-door, if necessary. People are more apt to learn if they are comfortable in their own surroundings as opposed to coming to some strange place to learn. Conventionally we want people to come to seminars, and to come here, do this, do that. But if people are not doing that, then we need to do something else. We, as health care professionals, need to go where people are! We are going to have to take a more active and assertive role in educating our people. They are not going to come to us, so we must go to them. We know that eight out of ten black people go to church. So we have to go to the church on Sunday and take the information there. We need to do whatever is needed to get the message out to black people.

I am particularly concerned about providing information about high blood pressure. This is one of my pet peeves. Black people have a high incidence of high blood pressure. I think some doctors, many times, do not promote vigorously enough the medical and treatment regime for high blood pressure. Many people, especially black people, with the ailment are not being monitored closely. They are not given the educational information they need regarding the diet, for instance. Many times people are referred to other professionals who do not obtain the patient's prior history or treatment record, and may duplicate medicines and treatment. Too often nobody follows up to see that the patient understands the importance of the medication or prescribed treatment.

What we don't know can definitely harm us. I was in Chicago talking with a group of African Americans about high blood pressure. I explained that high blood pressure and hypertension are the same. One little woman in the back of the room raised her hand and said, "Nurse, you are wrong! High blood pressure and hypertension are not the same thing. Let me tell you since you don't know. High blood pressure is when you have too much blood in your body and they need to take some of that blood out. Hypertension is, for example, when you are cooking something on the stove and the pot falls on the floor and you shake. That's hypertension!" I wanted to cry. I was so distressed. However, I could not convince this woman that high blood pressure and hypertension were the same condition. Although she said she had talked to a doctor, she obviously did not understand the information. I believe her reaction was not that unusual for many in the black community. This person does not know hypertension and high blood pressure are the same condition, does not understand what high blood pressure is. How are we going to teach her about her diet? About her medication? The importance of taking that medication daily on a regular basis? Had this woman with hypertension been my patient I would have informed her physician that she does not understand her diagnosis. I regret to this day that I did not pass on that information.

We need more public health nurses to go into people's homes to teach them about their disease, teach them about treatment, observe them, watch them cook, make sure that they take their medication and understand the side effects of the medication and the purpose of that medication. Naturally, it takes a little time, but in the long term, the effort will be invaluable. Medical costs and severe complications of the illness will be significantly reduced. The biggest benefit will be people's ability to take control over their own health care, in consultation with professionals.

Once we have more information we can take more control of our own care. If I were going to choose a disease to have, I would choose diabetes. As a diabetic I can control practically every aspect of my treatment. I can check my blood for an elevation of glucose, check my urine for various chemicals, follow or alter my diet, and give myself an insulin injection and not have to go into the doctor's office everyday to get my insulin injection. I'm taught about my skin care; I know to check my skin every day. If there's an open break in my skin, I know what I need to do. I can do all this. Because I feel a part of, and know what's going on with me, I can be an advocate for and take care of myself, provided I understand the proper care of my disease.

Unfortunately we've become so sophisticated in our delivery of health care we sometimes forget the people for whom the system is supposedly designed. It's nice to have a big marvelous clinic for people to come to, but if people have no transportation, no money to get there, we would have no patients. The problem of access is a critical one in our health care delivery system. Therefore, we need to do something differently when people are not doing what we, as health care professionals, want them to do. We need to change that system. If we, as professionals, can't change it, somehow we need to educate the consumers. As a motto at a local store here says: " A good shopper is an educated consumer."

My experience as a public health nurse and as a visiting nurse convinced me that we need to educate the consumer about health care. One solution a number of cities has implemented is an official Visiting Nurse Association. I thought it was superb in

Chicago. Patients would be referred to us, and we would go into their homes to teach them how to care for themselves, about their disease, about their medication, their diets, and so forth, right where they were. That way, we were not threatening. The patients were on their own turf rather than in a conventional hospital setting with strange people. They could throw us out at any time, and they would have some control over the situation. The public health nursing system is an excellent way of teaching patients in their own environment. We found that people responded.

On one supervisory visit to a private home, one of the nurses said, "Augusta, I need you to help me. I'm having problems. I cannot teach this man his diet." I soon discovered the nurse's error. The first step she should have taken was to determine where that person was in his understanding, his concerns. Upon talking to him, I learned that he had problems getting an erection. He was anxious about getting an appointment at the sexual dysfunction clinic at Cook County Hospital because he was more concerned about an erection than his diet. As I talked with him, I realized that his heart and mind were on getting to that clinic. I said, "Sir, do you want me to call that clinic and get an appointment for you?" He lit up like a Christmas tree! I made the appointment, much to his relief. *Then* he became interested in his diet, but only after what he perceived as his primary need and concern was taken care of. He was probably thinking, "Then I'll talk about what you want to talk about, the diet and my other health issues." People prioritize what is important to them, and trying to get to that erection clinic was important to him.

During the several years I worked for the Chicago Visiting Nurse Association I met Cora Lloyd, the only African American in the service with a highly visible management position. She was a real inspiration. Cora was forever encouraging us to go back to school to get a degree in nursing, and many of us did. Upon our graduation Cora anxiously sought us out and groomed us for management positions. It took me a while to follow her advice, but I look back now and thank her because I know now it was not easy for her to mentor and promote us as she did.

This preparation bolstered me for a tremendous career challenge in Chicago. My job was terminated along with the jobs of about a dozen other supervisors as a result of the consolidation of several district offices of the Visiting Nurse Service with the central office in the Loop. We were nurses of tenure: ten, thirteen, seventeen, and nineteen years of service. I looked at what had happened and said, "Something is wrong. Look at us. We are all past forty years old. Why don't we get some legal advice? We must act. They cannot take our jobs with no protest, no contest." Persons forty and above are in a protected group for employment. We were making top salaries, but the nurses being retained were younger nurses with fewer years of service, and, of course, making lower salaries.

About half our group went to get legal advice, but dropped out one by one. I knew something was fishy, so I persevered. At the age discrimination hearing, I won. The judge threw the case out because I did not show up.

I had not been informed of the court dates and by that time the New Zion Baptist Church of Louisville, Kentucky and its pastor, the Rev. Russell Akward, had hired me as the Director of Nursing at their James Taylor Memorial Nursing Home. I didn't mind so much since I knew the principle behind it was right, and I did see it through. We must stand up for ourselves.

The Taylor Nursing Home is marvelous proof that parishioners can have the assurance that when they grow old and can no longer live independently, they will be cared for by those who love and respect them.

It was there I met several people who supported me and had a strong emotional impact upon me, the kind of impact health care professionals often have the opportunity to provide. Bettye Johnson, a truly elegant woman, was executive director of the Taylor Home. She taught me much about the long-term care

Receiving a gift plant from the staff at the James Taylor Memorial Nursing Home, Louisville, 1986

industry. I was able to transfer many of these skills when I relocated to Salem, Massachusetts as Director of Discharge Planning at Salem Hospital. A second person, Margaret Harris, spiritually and physically beautiful, adopted me as her daughter. Ironically, she developed breast cancer and had a bilateral mastectomy three or four years after I did. She now tells me she knows I am her daughter because we had the same surgery, and my telephone call was the first one she received after her surgery. Wilma-Gene Bowman was another great help. She and I engaged in a baking business in Louisville, making cookies, pies, cakes and monkey bread which we sold to folks in the community. Baking became therapeutic for me, allowing me to take my mind away from the pressures and everyday stress, and lose myself. I still bake.

Chapter 12
Look At My Roots

If someone were to ask me now how I got where I am in terms of my emotional stability and how I feel about myself, I would say, "Look at my roots. Look where I came from; look at the interactions I had and what I went through to get where I am now."

I believe all of us are products of our environments. Perhaps a little more about my background can explain why I am who I am today. Then any reader, perhaps, but especially the African-American woman diagnosed with breast cancer, can see why I believe what I have learned on this journey is life-giving.

I was born in the small southern town of Ruston, Louisiana. My parents, Perry and Oleary Hasson Hicks, were natives of north Louisiana. We moved to San Pedro, California, during World War II where my father worked at the shipyard inspecting boats. He sustained an eye injury which resulted in his losing his sight later on in his life. My parents divorced when I was two years old, and my father remarried shortly afterwards. My stepmother was one of the greatest, most admired women that I know. She was an immaculate housekeeper, a wonderful role model who demonstrated order and neatness at all times.

I began school in California and continued in Louisiana after we moved back there in 1948. My father did not allow me to visit my mother or stay with her for a period of time. He was wise in his thinking, saying "Now, your mother has remarried, and sometimes it's not a good situation to have a stepdaughter in the household of another man." I can appreciate that now, but at that time I thought he was cruel and mean for not permitting me to go and stay with my mother.

I admire my mother's manner of handling the situation. She accepted the arrangement. When parents separate today, people say, repeatedly, "Oh, isn't that so sad for the children." It's not necessarily so sad for the children. What is sad for the children is when the parents cannot come to an agreement on who should have the responsibility for rearing that child. If it's agreed that the father will have the responsibility, then the mother should let that father raise that child. Not doing so can confuse the child.

I know the results of two parents in different households with different rules. This is where I was at one point. When I was with my mother she would say, "Do it this way, and it's okay for this." Then when I went back to my father, he would say, "Oh no. You don't do this." I wanted to say, "Will one of you back off and just let one person tell me what to do!" I did not do that, of course, but I learned from that experience that if I were ever in that situation I would not allow that to happen to my child; I would be open to allowing one parent to raise that child.

The other parent should be supportive, however. He or she is not out of the picture. Divorce does not end parenthood. The child needs support: parents must collaborate, make sure the child is nurtured. They must support each other to avoid harming the child. If the non-custodial parent wants a change, then he or she should speak with the other parent, not the child, about the change.

I can speak because my parents did not have a collaborative arrangement, but I think my mother handled it as gracefully as she knew how. Both had their own agenda on how a child should be raised, and that's where the confusion arose. That's where it could be said, "Oh, it's so sad for the children." Separation and divorce happen. But neither should have a very negative impact upon the child.

When my father considered me old enough to protect and defend myself, which was in my senior year in high school, he allowed me to go visit my mother. It was quite a joyous celebration because that was the first time I can recall my brothers and I being with my mom as a unit. She would write to me, and

At my maternal grandfather Henry Hasson's house, Jonesboro, Louisiana, about 1950

occasionally I would speak with her on the telephone, but that was about the extent of the time I spent with her.

As it did with my parents, school played an important role in my life. I was terrified to go to school. I started Lincoln High School, the local school for African Americans, the February I was six years old. Until that time my parents taught me at home, so I knew my alphabet, and I could count. My parents were able to demonstrate this to the principal, so he permitted me to start in February. During that time from February to May, there were too many children in the first grade, so we were sent to the second grade. We sat in a little row of seats on the side of the wall doing second grade work, and at the end of the year, we were passed to the third grade.

Going through grade school was, for the most part, uneventful, but in the fifth or sixth grade, we had a career day. Each student expressed her or his career aspirations. I had seen nurses when my father was ill in the hospital. When my friends and I played, one of them always wanted to be the teacher, and I wanted to be the nurse. So, on that day I said "I want to be a nurse," and there were several other students who said the same. I remember saying, "Oh, I'm going to have some company. I'm going to have other nurses that I know with me." That stayed with me all those years that I wanted to be a nurse.

We saw some of our teachers seven days a week. We saw

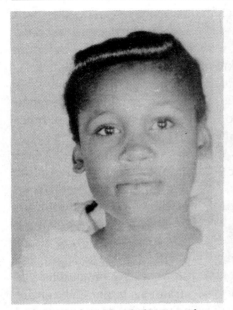

By the time this school photograph was taken in 1952, I knew that I wanted to be a nurse.

our teachers at school, and we saw them in the community. When we went to church, our teachers were there. Our English teacher, Mr. Carl Donald Whitmyer, was our choir director and accompanist. Our elementary school principal, Mr. Albert McHenry, was the superintendent of the Sunday School. If one of the teachers saw any one of us misbehave, that teacher would chastise us and then follow up by discussing the issue with our parents. Then our parents would address the issue with us.

Education was extremely important in our home because my parents wanted our lives to be better than theirs. They wanted to make sure we were prepared to be gainfully employed, have financial stability, and be able to enjoy some of the finer things in life that they didn't have an opportunity to enjoy. I can recall my father saying, "Nothing is going to be handed to you on a gold platter. You have to work hard, and it will pay off."

Our house was located in the center of the community institutions. I could stand on my front porch and see the church building and hear the church bell ring for services. I lived next door to the high school principal, J. K. Haynes, who was much respected among black people for standing up for them at a perilous time in our history, and who was twice injured for violation of some of the racial mores of the South. He fought for equality in education and encouraged each one of us to excel. He was instrumental in bringing the first African American physician, Dr. Cyril Waldron, to our small community. He brought great teachers and speakers to the community. I recall Mary McCleod Bethune, founder of the Bethune-Cookman College and influential member of Franklin D. Roosevelt's Black Brain Trust, speaking to us at school. I was spellbound and more determined than ever to become a registered nurse, not a nurse's aide or a licensed practical nurse, but a *registered* nurse.

Several of our teachers lived in my neighborhood. There were six ministers – C. C. McLain, C. D. Simmons, C. P. Payne, my father, Perry Hicks, David W. Smith, and the elderly Rev. Robert Lewis – all living within a block of us. We could have had a little seminary there. I couldn't get away with much mischief.

We had a lot of support growing up. Mrs. Clara Jackson Carr lived not far away. She was a teacher and a supervisor of schools in Jackson Parish to the south of us. One of the little-known facets of civil rights history is the role of unsung men and women, like Clara Carr, in areas removed from the spotlight, who worked quietly instructing other black people in the parish on voting procedures. She took us to church conventions and association meetings. She would see to it that we participated in programs. Other people did the same. I will always remember such people as Shellie Hall, the father of all girls, who spent a lot of time taking the boys to activities such as hayrides, hikes, and baseball games. I have no doubt that these experiences set the stage for our development into the contributing citizens that most of us turned out to be.

Church and the people there have always been significant. My parents told me that as a little girl I would cry whenever the minister delivered his message. I don't know why I cried; perhaps I was touched by the sermon. One of the elderly women of the church told my parents that my "little soul" was happy, and I guess it was. In spite of the pretty dress and special treats my parents promised me if I didn't cry in church, I still cried.

My faith and trust in God which began in my youth has made the experience with cancer bearable. I have many favorite scripture passages that I read to increase my strength to march forward. A constant reminder of God's help is in Isaiah 40:31 – "But they that wait upon the Lord shall renew their strength; they shall mount up with wings as eagles; they shall run and not get weary; and they shall walk and not faint." I have waited on the Lord, given Him my wants, and He has answered. Sometimes I draw on the spiritual I learned as a child to "have a little talk with Jesus and tell Him all about my troubles. He will answer by and by." I talk with God daily. My favorite places are in the bathroom on my aching knees and on my daily walks.

Another comforting phrase for my triumph over breast cancer was "Things will be better tomorrow." When tomorrow came, if I did not feel 100%, I assured myself I would feel better tomorrow. Tomorrow came the day I was without pain, put my head in the air, and was proud and pleased with how I looked and felt and was able to share my experience with others.

At an early age I was given explanations which have given me the strength to persevere. I remember asking my father why doesn't God speak to the people today as He did in the past, like in the burning bush or in the parting Red Sea. My father hesitated, and then he answered me by saying, "My daughter, God does speak to people as He did in the past, but we are not listening to Him. We are always in a hurry and just don't heed His works or signs."

Always believing him, I gave my life to Christ when I was about nine years old. At the annual revival at our church, a guest evangelist would preach and win souls for God. I recall sitting up front on what was called the "mourner's bench" with my playmates Pat McLain, Mae Hall, Doyce Foster, Nettie Streets, Mattie Diamond, Velma Westbrook, and Martha Roberts when I made the decision to join the church. I think I was the first to make the decision, and the others followed. I took this step very seriously. The older members of the church and my parents told me, "Now that you are a little Christian, you are not to steal and tell little stories (they never said 'lie,') and you must go to church every Sunday." Going to church meant attending Sunday School, morning worship service, Baptist Training Union, and evening services, as well as a mid-week prayer and other services. I taught Sunday School, sang in the church choir, and even taught a Baptist Training Union class. (I continued this practice until I graduated from high school in 1958.)

When I became a teenager, I didn't want to attend B. T. U. at 6:00 p. m. every Sunday because most of my friends were dancing and socializing at a little hangout on "The Front," the street where most of the community's commercial establishments were located. Friends would see me going to church for the B. T. U., but I wanted so much to go to The Cafe. Now I look back on this experience as increasing my faith and trust in God. I think if some of my friends had been in church with me then, they might have had a different mindset in dealing with some of the problems they have faced, and with different outcomes.

My very protective father tried to make sure that we did not get out with the wrong crowd. He and my stepmother were very concerned about that. We did not have a high teenage pregnancy rate when I grew up. In the case of the few who became pregnant, the girls in my group were not permitted to associate with them. At this point in my life I think that was wrong because those young women lost much-needed support. With hindsight, I don't believe that was the right thing to do, but at that time I had no choice. I was an obedient child. I wanted to please my parents. I really didn't know anything else to do but to please them. I pleased them by going to church and school and obeying their wishes.

In 1954 my father lost his eyesight, just as I was going into high school. He had been losing his vision all along, but we were unaware of it because he never told us until his condition had progressed to the point that it became obvious. One night when we were coming from a church in the country, my father drove

My oldest brother, Perry, just after he won the Fresno Golden Glove boxing championship, about 1955

off the highway. And he said, "Oh, I didn't see that."

When we got home, he sat us down and told us that he had been losing his vision over a period of time. A young man with the responsibility of a family with three children, he was as stern as ever: "I have a family to support. I'm still the head of my household, and I have to provide." He quickly pulled himself together and enrolled in the school for blind African Americans at Scotlandville, near Southern University in south Louisiana. He learned to read braille so that he could communicate, and he learned a trade making brooms, mops, and doormats so that he would have a steady income.

From my father's way of accomodating his blindness I learned that life goes on and we must prepare ourselves to keep marching. He did not succumb or give in to his handicap. I learned a lot about faith and trust in God from my father. He pulled himself together, made an assessment of what he needed to do, and moved forward. The business did well. We did door-to-door peddling on Saturday. He would never let his business interfere with our education. If we had brooms or mops to deliver, he would tell his clients he would deliver them on Saturday because he knew we would be free.

Not surprisingly, we learned from my father's challenge. I did not actually learn to make brooms, but I helped out with some of the chores. My brother, Henry, learned the process so well that he could have begun his own business. When my older brother Perry was barely in his teens, he ran away and hitchhiked from Louisiana to California to be with our mother. Although he was six when my parents divorced, he wanted to return to California to be with her. He has been in California most of his life and has lived in Mexico near the border for years. Very fluent in Spanish, he has spoken it for such a long time that he can barely speak English now. But he didn't get the first hand business experience that Henry and I were exposed to by helping our dad. Other than this, I did not have any work experience in Louisiana. As it turned out, Henry has operated two successful businesses. Thanks to his learning the saxophone in high school, he has led jazz bands and played with bands in the army and in New York nightclubs.

Now that I've had some exposure to occupational hazards, I realize that we were at risk and didn't know it because the yarn for each mop was cut individually, and the lint and the particles were flying in the air. No doubt we could have easily inhaled them. We don't seem to have any residual effects from it, but we would wear a mask and use protective gear now.

Henry and I graduated from Lincoln High School in 1958. He joined the army in the early 1960s.

The business did well. We received large contracts from Grambling State University, and several other black schools gave us orders. We would work over the weekend, and late at night, and would tell my father, "Oh, Daddy, it's time to go to bed; it's dark." His reply: "Well, it's dark to me all the time. Keep working."

As we worked as a unit, we would discuss family concerns.

I got my driver's license at a very early age so that I could drive for my father, and I was excited just to be able to drive in those days. My father had taught me to drive, unintentionally, when he was actually instructing my brothers.

We had a 1954 black Chevrolet with a standard shift, and he would take them out as part of spending time with us children. He began teaching them the basics of driving – steering the car and how to shift and change gears. All the time I was sitting in the back seat just observing. One day when we were about two blocks from home, I said, "Let me drive."

Both my brothers laughed. They turned around. *"You* drive?!" I said, "Sure, I can drive."

Not believing me, they said okay. I convinced them. I got in the driver's seat, shifted the gears, and drove home! I proved what I could do at an early age. I knew I could do it. This was part of a pattern leading up from my childhood to where I am now.

My father stressed self-sufficiency. Before I went to nursing school he killed one of our chickens and had me to clean it and cut it into various parts. He said he wanted me to get accustomed to seeing the inside of a living creature, the organs and intestines, because he knew that I would be exposed to these kinds of things in school. When we got to school, we dissected cats. Remembering the chicken, I thought, "This man is pretty much together."

Some of my family migrated to Chicago during the 1936 World's Fair to better their working conditions and lifestyles. They all succeeded. What I knew about nursing schools I got from an aunt, Mattie Hicks, and a cousin, Archie Rice, who came from Chicago to Louisiana to visit. I wrote for information and applications. Provident in Chicago was the first school to respond. I don't remember whether the other hospitals actually sent applications or not, but I was accepted at Provident. Several people, including Mrs. Arnetta Willis, a neighbor of ours, wrote reference letters for me. When I got to school someone mentioned to me that there was one lady from

Aunt Mattie Hicks moved to Chicago in 1936. She is seen here in a passport picture just before she visited Europe in 1979.

my community – Mrs. Willis – who thought I was "super, excellent, a very nice person, a very honest person."

Provident Hospital and Nursing School were established in the late 19th century at a time when much of life in America was segregated. It came into being after a young black woman came to Chicago from Kansas City to study nursing and was turned down by the established nursing schools in the city because of her race. I understand that those early student nurses were not allowed to have rooms on the regular floors. Their sleeping quarters were in the basement of Cook County Hospital when they were there for their practical experience. A couple of African American doctors became aware of her difficulties and that of other young black women who sought to become nurses and formed a coalition of local folk who managed to establish a small hospital and nurses' training school. The facility was small, but it had very high standards. The School of Nursing has closed, and the hospital has been rebuilt on the same block after merging with Cook County Hospital.

Provident was the site of the first open heart surgery in the United States. In 1893 a man who was stabbed in an altercation in the neighborhood was rushed into the hospital, and Dr. Daniel Hale Williams, one of the founders, actually opened his chest wall, exposed his heart, and sutured it back together. In Provident's lobby I was inspired by the display of the instruments that Dr. Williams used for this historic event.

I was terrified my first day at Provident because I had been so protected growing up. First, I had to get used to living with a group of females. That was a big adjustment for me as I had grown up the only girl with two brothers. Another difference was the greater diversity of people. In our small southern town we never saw immigrants. The housemother at Provident was a Haitian who spoke heavily accented English. I had to become accustomed to the way she spoke. I wasn't overwhelmed, though, and I soon adjusted and eventually successfully completed the program.

The Chicago snow and ice were something else, however. I fell on the snow and severely injured my ankle, tearing ligaments. My ankle swelled; my leg was uncomfortable; I still had to care for patients in the hospital. I tried to keep going with a cast but finally decided that I should wait until the ankle healed before continuing.

I took a leave of absence and returned to Louisiana. I didn't sit around, though. My father said, "You're here, but you need to continue studying. You don't have to go on the floor to work and take care of people, so just study to keep up." I enrolled in science and mathematics courses at Grambling State University, seven miles from my hometown. I returned to Provident and finished in 1963.

My parents could not afford to send me much of an allowance, so I made extra money to buy what I needed by doing a variety of tasks. Styling the hair of other student nurses was one. I'll never forget my first attempt at cutting hair. Ada White from Alabama asked me to cut her hair. I had never ever cut anyone's

hair before. I got my scissors and proceeded. I cut her hair one-
sided; one side was up, and the other was down. It looked as if I
had put an uneven bowl on her head and cut around it. If I had
been my "patron," I would have gotten out of that chair and beaten
me unmercifully. I polished shoes for the upper classwomen because they especially liked the way I did them. I always wanted
things neatly done and in place, and I had a unique method for
doing shoes. It was established practice to have a clear black line
of demarcation around the heel of the nurses' white shoes. I would
put a piece of tape around the heel and make the black line and
then polish and buff the uppers. The shoes looked like patent
leather when I finished them. I had always been taught to do the
best in whatever I did. Of course, the upper classwomen didn't

*Graduation, Provident Hospital and Nurse's
Training School, Chicago, 1963*

have money, either. They would pay me with a bar of soap or a tube of toothpaste. I wasn't supposed to be smoking, but I did, so they would someimes pay me with a package of cigarettes. I continued these little jobs the whole time I was in nursing school.

Among the thirty-five students who began the class, only nine of us graduated. Almost all of us were from the southern United States. We were strong; we endured; we presevered. Some of the students who did not finish seemed to have trouble settling down to curfews and constant studying. My background and the ability to impose some self-discipline were important in my success. I was later told that someone had said, "Here's a little girl coming from a small town; she's going to run amuck." But they didn't know me, or my goal. I received three of the six awards bestowed on graduates of the program: scholastic honors; Body Mechanics (proper moving and lifting techniques); and neatness (in proper uniform at all times.)

My proud parents came to my graduation, and so did my relatives in the Chicago area.

My new husband, Everett Sullivan, came, too. Student nurses were not supposed to marry while in training. A couple of months before the end of the school year, I got married and never revealed it to a single person until the night of graduation. Being a southern girl, I called my parents and asked permission to get married. They said, "No," I did "not need to get married." But I decided to show them at that point that I could get married. I said to myself, "I am a grown lady now, and I can do what I want." I had been reared to think that when a person became sexually involved with someone, the two should marry because the relationship was serious. Everett was my first sexual partner. So I married him, a freckled-faced man from Mississippi, who ran a big night club in Chicago. I introduced him as my husband to my parents, and I think my mother cried. I guess she felt that I'd been in school, restricted, and that I needed to have freedom to explore the world and its possibilities, but I wanted to get married.

Needless to say, that marriage did not last very long because I was not mature enough to be married at that time. I don't think Everett was either, although this was his second marriage. I did not feel he was supportive of my goals. He was extremely possessive, too, so I left him shortly after we were married.

I remembered my father's words of long ago: "Get an education so that in the event that you marry and things do not work out, you can be self-sufficient. You can leave, and you can make it." My father was right. I have had three stormy marriages.

There were certain sections of Chicago that African Americans migrated to, and there were areas where they infiltrated over time. African Americans were many places in large numbers. By the time I was employed, various ethnic groups in a variety of professions were represented in the work force.

Chapter 13
If Others Can Do It So Can I

My first job after graduation was in the Emergency Room at Cook County Hospital.

I chose that hospital because I wanted to go someplace where I could get lots of experience, and I thought I would be able to see everything and would learn quickly. Cook County is a large teaching hospital with a huge campus; the medical staff was from all over the world.

The emergency room was set up like no other emergency room I've ever seen. All the male patients entered on one side, and all the female patients entered on the other. In the center was a surgical dispensary where all the lacerations and gunshot wounds were seen. The big adjustment from being a student nurse one day and working as a graduate nurse the next day was very strange, very new, very different. I had never seen so many people waiting in an emergency room – two or three hundred people sitting in the waiting areas, waiting for care. After orientation on the first night, I worked from 3:00 p. m. until 11:00 p. m. The next day I returned for the same shift; some of the same people were still sitting there waiting to see a doctor! I couldn't believe it!

The first day I worked so hard I nearly forgot to take my lunch break. I asked a nurse who was working with me, "When do you go to eat around this place? Do you ever go, or do you just work the whole shift?"

She said, "Oh, the schedule is in the back." I was still accustomed to being a student nurse who was told what time to eat as well as what time to do everything else. Finally I went to lunch.

When I came back the next day, I went to the divisional director's office and told her I wanted a transfer. She wanted to know why.

I said, "I don't think this is what I want."

"Well, just give yourself some time. You're a new grad, and I'm sure all this is totally different for you."

When I went home and thought about it, I came back the next day and said, "If these nurses are here, they had to make the adjustment, and so can I."

I stayed and worked, and within three months I was promoted to Head Nurse. This experience has been a guide to me throughout my career. When I'm having doubts or difficulties, or go into a new situation, I always remind myself: "Remember how difficult it was for you at Cook County Hospital? Remember how you felt then? Remember what you did? You pulled yourself together and you moved forward." Before I undertake anything challenging, I always reflect on this experience.

There was much that disturbed me at Cook County Hospital. After I was promoted to Head Nurse, I would make rounds and find people sitting in wheelchairs or on the floor, dead. It was such a busy place, and I guess we just didn't have the proper help. That really disturbed me because these were human beings. That situation was corrected later by bringing on more staff and reorganizing the emergency treatment process.

One of my responsibilities as a newly promoted Head Nurse was to keep track of medical instruments in the Emergency Room. Some doctors would walk through and pick up instruments and not return them. Sure enough, a physician came through and took some insturments. "You're not supposed to take those instruments," I said.

He looked at me. And I think because he was white and I was a nurse of color, he said, "You watch me. You stop me."

I was terrified. I had never had anyone speak to me like that. I cried all the way home on the bus because this doctor had talked to me like that. My only comfort was the Bible verse "They that wait upon the Lord shall renew their strength." So, I waited.

Three years later, the same doctor was in the emergency room, and a patient came in with a diagnosis of asthma. All the asthma patients were put together in a large waiting room. The doctor would come in and examine them and order medication, and the patients would remain there until they were breathing easier. This doctor went to a little restaurant across the street from the hospital while the patient waited. I phoned him three times, each time saying the patient was having trouble. He finally returned and examined the patient; and she was dead. He then ordered me, "Give her a shot of epinephrine."

I said, "I will NOT! If you want her to have it, you give it to her!"

He looked up in surprise. I don't know if he remembered the incident with the instruments, but I reported him to the administrator, and he was suspended. That was just a little slap on the finger, for that doctor's patient had died. As far as I was concerned, he should have been fired and never ever allowed to practice medicine again.

I started to assert myself around this time, and that's about when I began to learn that physicians should not be on pedestals; I can challenge them. So can you. This was good for me in the long haul because I was able to challenge doctors later. They are human beings, and they sometimes make errors. The patient has the right to question.

Chapter 14
Challenges and Competencies

When I left the emergency room, I went into a different kind of practice, Occupational Health. I worked with Zenith Radio Corporation and Sunbeam and later was a staff nurse at the University of Chicago Billings Hospital.

I met Victor Berry, my second husband, when I was employed at Zenith. He was a tall, handsome, Harry Belafonte-looking West Indian. Someone there told him that there was a West Indian nurse working in the medical department. So, of course, he came dashing in, looking at me. I'm a person of African descent; he's a person of African descent. Maybe he couldn't tell by looking at me if I was West Indian or not, but when I opened my mouth, he knew right away.

"You're not West Indian. You no Jamaican."

"Never said I was."

From that wary start we developed a relationship and were married in 1967. Our son, and my only child, Byron Barrington Berry, was born a year later.

While I was at Zenith, there were a few trying incidents. This is when I started paying attention to white people who challenge black management on the job, always questioning our judgement. Employees worked on the lines, installing various parts on the chassis in the television. The chassis had sharp little projectiles, and the workers would sometimes injure themselves. They had to come to the nurse if there was a tear in the skin because Occupational Safety and Health Administration (OSHA) required that all injuries be logged.

Byron is reluctant to get his photograph made during my parents' visit to Chicago in 1969.

One of the foremen called me on the telephone and said: "Call the ambulance. I'm sending an employee there. She is very ill. You need to call the ambulance to get her out."

I replied, "You send her here and let me make that decision. That's why I'm here. I don't come on the line making decisions about your job." He needed only say, "I am sending an employee." If, indeed, she was so seriously ill or injured, with a broken leg or arm, or bleeding, say, he would have requested me to come to the area.

The employee came in, and she was fighting desperately to keep her eyes closed, blinking her eyes. I knew right away that she was in no distress because she was struggling to keep her eyes closed and did not demonstrate any symptoms of distress. I sent everyone out of the medical department. I told her, "Okay. Get off the stretcher now and tell me what's wrong."

She said, "Well, I wanted to go to the bathroom and no one relieved me, so I just sat on the floor like I had passed out."

I said, "Well, okay. Why don't you get up and go in the back and relax, and get yourself together and go back to work."

"Ohhh! You're going to send me back to work!"

"Absolutely. There's nothing wrong." I explained to her about the absentee tally that the foremen kept when employees had to leave the job, and she decided that she would return.

I called the foreman and said, "I'm sending the employee back to work."

"What do you mean? There's nothing wrong with her? She was on the floor sick."

I said, "Listen. Hear me. I have examined the employee and find no problems and also she has admitted there is nothing wrong and why she sat on the floor. I'm in charge here in the medical department. You're in charge of those assembly lines." Our relationship eventually improved.

This questioning of my ability followed me. When I left Zenith I went to Sunbeam. Apparently they had never seen a black RN at that company. Taken on a tour, I noticed people stopping their work, particularly white people, to turn around and look as though I were something from outer space! A year later I began to work for the Department of Health for a number of years. During my tenure there not only was I challenged on the management level, but as a clinical nurse, a staff nurse. For example, the supervisor showed no respect for black nurses. Because of a number of negative experiences I had when I worked at a Board of Health clinic run by the city for children and pregnant women, I was somewhat prepared or at least better prepared than I would have been.

One day a laundry man came in to pick up the laundry. The supervisor instructed him, "Go in the back and see that big, black, colored girl back there and get the laundry from her."

I immediately went to the "big, black, colored girl" and said, "Let me tell you what your boss thinks about you. She referred to you as a "big, black, colored girl." This large, dark-skinned woman came out and informed the supervisor, telling her in no uncertain terms, that she had a name and she expected the supervisor to use it. Size nor color had nothing to do with her job description.

Of course, the supervisor denied having made the remark. Sitting in the same room at the adjacent desk, I said: "Oh no! I heard you say that.!"

There were other incidents that seemed to be racially motivated, so I got the nurses together, particularly the black nurses, and said, "Look, I am not going to tolerate this. I suggest we do something about it. Let's get together, write our complaints and send them in to the executive director." They agreed and asked me to write the letter.

I detailed all our complaints in the letter. There were about fifteen nurses in that office. About ten of them signed the letter, and the rest backed out. "No. I'm not signing anything like that. You think I'm going to get in trouble? You're on your own."

I said, "Fine."

One of the nurses told the supervisor that I had a letter complaining about her. She called me in for a conference and said, "I know you have this letter, and I want to tell you, nobody's going to stand behind you. You send that letter in, and it's going to be you by yourself."

I said, "I'll take my chances."

I walked out of her office, walked out the front door. There was a mailbox right in front of a big glass window in front of the building. I opened the mailbox, turned around to make sure she saw me, and dropped the letter in.

Immediately the next morning she came to me. "Augusta, now, you're a good nurse. Down at the administrative office I told them what a good nurse you are." I agreed, but told her it was not going to change my position. The group in support of the letter had called the headquarters earlier to set up an appointment, but nobody responded to us. But when they got that letter the next day, all of us who signed the letter were called in.

We went down and talked about each complaint. I thought

the other nurses might get there and get lockjaw and not open their mouths, but everybody spoke freely, and we got everything out on the table. Then at the end the director said, "Augusta, what do you think we should do with the supervisor?"

I said, "You know, that's really your decision. I'm just pointing out the facts to you. You do what you think best for the organization."

In two weeks that supervisor was transferred to another office. However, my performance evaluation was due shortly after she left, and she said, "Oh, I will come back and evaluate Augusta." Her revenge meant a poor evaluation for me, including false accusations, one of which was that I didn't know my job.

When I saw her evaluation, I wadded it up, but then I said, "No. This is what she expects," so I smoothed the paper out, turned it over, and evaluated her. I gave it to her. And I do not think she ever submitted that first evaluation.

Prior to that episode there was a practice of pulling nurses from one clinic to help at another clinic when they were short. One day they needed help at the Lead Clinic, and I was asked to go. But I did not use any nursing skills. I just stood there and held the babies on the table while the doctors drew blood.

The next day they wanted to send me back. I refused. I told the supervisor, "You don't need an RN to go there. You need a nurse's aide to go."

When she saw that I was adamant about not going, she insisted, in spite of my protest, that I go home, just as simple as that.

I decided to see the executive director, but before I went, I called back to see who had been sent to the Lead Clinic, and sure enough, a nurse's aide had been sent. Since I didn't have an appointment, I waited about thirty minutes. People were walking in and out, and finally they called me in. Of course, the supervisor had called the office to tell them what had happened, and that they had sent me home.

When I walked in, they asked me, "Why are you here? You were sent home." I said, "I am not a child. I'd like to discuss the issues. An RN was not needed at that station to hold a baby while the doctor drew blood. You needed a nurse's assistant. And if you check, that's who was sent there, a nurse's assistant."

"Well...," they hesitated. They said, "Well, you have to go home."

I said, "Okay."

I left the building, and I sat in full uniform on the bench right outside of the window so that they could see me. I wanted passers-by to wonder: "Why is a nurse sitting out there on that bench all day instead of being at one of the clinics?"

I called a friend, explained what had happened, and instructed him to call and ask why that nurse is sitting out there. I asked him to call everybody he knew, and have them call and ask the same thing. I could tell when someone would call because people in the building would come to the window and look.

The next morning when I got to work, my supervisor called me and said, "Oh, I just want you to know you'll be paid for yesterday."

In the course of working at various places I noticed that the nurses with college degrees were not on the floor working so hard, and I remembered Cora Lloyd's advice from long ago. I said, "Get smart." I had been out of nursing school ten or twelve years before I went back to school to get a bachelor's degree from Governor's State University in Chicago.

Due to my long hours of study and work, my marriage to Victor began to unravel. We were divorced several months before my graduation.

I happened to be at the right place at the right time for graduate school at the University of Illinois School of Public Health; I received a full scholarship which paid my tuition and all my expenses.

I did not do well on the Graduate Records Examination, and I had gone to an undergraduate school which had a pass or fail grading system. The University of Illinois did not want to accept the "pass-fail" system but wanted to see an A or a B. So there was some question whether I would be accepted or not, but there was a possibility of getting in because of my background. I went in to speak with the dean who said, "Well, you didn't score very high on your GRE."

I said, "You are correct, but please allow me to share a few things with you. There is not one single question on that test regarding nursing and my background. But I have these competencies." A competency statement was part of the criteria for admission. I explained to him some of my strengths and some of the courses I had taken that enabled me to excel at my work. For example, I had completed a course in the legal aspect of nursing and knew how to look up cases and research information. "Challenge me. Ask me something about nursing."

"Ohhh. I don't know anything about nursing," he said.

I said, "Okay. It's just like that examination I took. There was nothing on there about nursing, and I didn't know a lot of the things they were talking about. I had not had that exposure.

Graduation, Governor's State University, Park Forest South, Illinois, where I received a bachelor of Science in Nursing degree, 1980

When I asked you to challenge me and ask me something about nursing, you didn't know anything about it because you haven't had that training and experience. The same thing here." I was accepted into the graduate school.

I did have problems with one class: bio-statistics. However, I needed to pass that class. So I went out and found two tutors. The white instructor had written the textbook, and it was generally stated that his belief was that black people would not pass his course. According to this thinking one side of our brain was not developed to handle complex calculations such as those required to learn bio-stats. I got through his course. It was the only "C" I made in graduate school, but to me it seemed like an "A," just to get out of that course! I am happy to report that my fellow black classmates passed the course, too.

The other course I was told I would have trouble with was epidemiology. The professor came to me and said, "You are going to have problems because you barely got through bio-statistics." What did I make in epidemiology? An "A." It was practical. It was nursing. It was something that I did on a daily basis.

There were other problems and challenges, but I was goal-directed, and did what I needed to succeed. I graduated with a Masters in Public Health in 1981.

All four of us black students were looked upon as being different by the white students. They would look at us and make remarks such as, "We were fine until they got here!" I couldn't believe this was going on in the 1980s, but it was, and still we accomplished what we set out to do.

Chapter 15
My First Bout With Cancer

I was diagnosed with chondrosarcoma of the right tibia in 1984. I was in Provident Hospital with pain in my back. Having been an avid tennis player, I had had an orthoscopic examination of my knee several years earlier. As the doctor was taking my medical history during hospitalization for the back pain, he said, "Well, let me just take an x-ray of your knee and see what's going on."

The next day he came to my room with the x-ray report and questioned me about whether I now had, or had had in the past, pain in my leg.

I said, "No. What's the matter?"

He informed me that the x-ray had picked up a tumor in my leg. I snatched the x-ray report from his hand and read "a star-like irregular shaped tumor seen." I knew automatically that was cancerous because benign – or noncancerous – tumors are smooth edged and not irregular in shape, but malignant tumors are irregularly shaped and not well defined. So I asked the doctor what he was going to do. He said, "The first thing we need to do is have a biopsy."

I said, "Okay, do it today."

This was an older doctor who had taught me in nursing school. He preferred that I have a younger doctor do the procedure. I was transferred to Mercy Hospital where the young doctor worked. Although I did not know him, his doctor father and I had worked together at Provident Hospital. I explained to him that before I agreed to be his patient I needed a doctor who would take time with me and let me be a part of what was going on. He stayed about half an hour on that first visit, and I finally told him, "You may go, Dr. Williams."

When he left, a young white intern came in. "We're gonna have an x-ray; we're gonna have a blood test; we're gonna have this; we're gonna have that." I told him that since I'd just had all these tests at another hospital, it was not necessary to repeat them here.

"Well, we can't accept that from the other hospital." Flabbergasted, I saw his single-mindedness at work. But I was just as single-minded. Now, I've moved from a predominantly black hospital to a predominantly white hospital with a white intern, and my primary doctor is a black doctor. The young intern said, "We can't accept that."

I said, "Why? They are the same tests done in this hospital, the same methods of testing, the same processes. Now tell me why you can't accept them."

"Well, we just can't."

I said, "I'll go get them for you."

And then he went on to talk, never doubting he could make me agree with his assessment. When he realized that I would not change my mind, he evaded the issue, asking me, "Oh, why do you have an attitude?"

Seething now, I countered with, "I'm concerned about doctors who have very poor bedside manners, who don't take into consideration the feelings of patients."

He responded, "You should be worried about that tumor in your leg, whether it's cancerous or not. That's what you should be doing."

This is what happens sometimes when patients speak up for themselves. Too many doctors say the patients are crazy, have an attitude, or any number of statements designed to make patients mistrust their own judgment. He ran out to the nurses' station and said, "That lady in there is crazy." But he canceled the x-ray and the blood work and never mentioned the test again. Later on he became a partner with me and collaborated with me in my treatment plan.

When my primary physician came in on a daily basis, he would sit in a chair or on my bed, and together we would discuss my treatment and progress. Because Christmas was near he wanted me to go home because surgery is generally not done until after Christmas. By this time I had married a clinical psychologist, Dr. Andrew Gale, but things were going badly between us. I had not prepared for Christmas, and I would have been more depressed going home.

The day after Christmas the doctor came in and told me he was going to take me to surgery and remove the tumor in my leg. If it was benign, some bone from my left hip would replace the bone in my leg. If it was malignant, ..."

I interrupted him. "Okay, doctor. You do nothing. Wait and come and discuss with me my options the next day," and he agreed. I had to set up a partnership with the doctor, and I felt comfortable telling him what I wanted to do.

I was given a surgical consent form to sign. After a careful reading, I was satisfied that the doctors had the procedure down pat. But I wrote on the form exactly what we had discussed: "If the tumor is benign, remove some bone tissue from the hip and replace it. It if's malignant, do nothing. Let me make the decision later." I signed my name. This agreement was honored in the operating room.

The biopsy came back benign. All I could say was, "Thank you, God, it's noncancerous."

Although I had a cast from my toe to my upper thigh, I seemed to be doing fine, recuperating. Then one day the doctor came in looking very sad. I could pick up his mood. I said, "Oh, Dr. Wlliams, what's wrong now?"

He said, "Augusta, we sent that specimen to Sloan-Kettering. They picked up low-grade cancer cells."

All I could say was, "Dr. Williams, would you please go away. I want to be alone; come back tomorrow, and I'll talk to you." He left.

The next day, he informed me of Dr. Ralph Marcove's stunning success with cryosurgery, the use of liquid nitrogen to destroy cancer cells. I was impressed with the statistics he presented and immediately agreed to go to Sloan-Kettering for this procedure.

Most of my loved ones responded well. Byron, my son, was still very young then. He had asked his father if I were going to die and been assured that I would be all right. That's all I can remember my son expressing about my illness, but he came to visit me in the hospital frequently, sometimes with his friends. Because I was divorced from his father, and married again, Byron's father did not come. Several of my friends made regular visits, and that helped me to keep up my morale.

My husband, however, would not visit me when I was in the hospital in Chicago and refused to visit me or make contact with me in New York. Not surprisingly, I felt all alone and became quite depressed. Andrew Gale was a brilliant man, but he had his own views about life and how one should interact with others. He did not visit me during this illness nor any other illness that I had. He never called me during this entire episode, so before I left New York I called his mother and asked her if I might stay with her when I returned to Chicago. She readily consented.

My family and friends were quite concerned about Andrew's lack of support for me. They went out of their way to cheer me up and help me in spite of the difficulty in doing so. My sweet little friend Sarah Richmond Mayfield from Ruston came all the way across Chicago on the bus on one of the coldest days of the year to bring me fried chicken. Of course, it was nearly frozen when she got it to me, but I will always remember her kindness. Dear Emma Carruthers visited me every single day while I was in the hospital in spite of serious personal problems of her own and never mentioned a word about them.

I encourage you to call your friends when they are hospitalized because it is lonely being hospitalized. You are taken away from family and loved ones. Call and say hello, I was thinking about you. Send a get well card, forewarn them you are coming, and visit for a short period. Please don't ask, "What's your problem?" The patient will tell you in time if she or he wants to share it with you.

Many people called me: Vincent and Betty Crawford called from Las Vegas, Andy and Margaret Hankins called from Detroit to cheer me. Many of my church family members and my minister, Dr. Alfloyd Butler called to pray and wish me well. My friend Juanita Thomas, who is an RN and worked at Mercy Hospital, visited me daily and brought special ethnic food for me. My cousins Shirley, Bonnie and Barbara Moore called to wish me well.

Once my parents were informed of my illness, they called me nearly everyday. Upon finding out that I was going to New York for treatment, my mom sent my airfare immediately. I think I was somewhat in a state of shock regarding this illness because I was so frightened that something abnormal was growing in my body and that there was no manifestation of it. I am so thankful to this day I shared with Dr. Proffitt that I had had an orthoscopic exam some time ago and that he followed up by taking an x-ray. It is important to share with your doctor when he is taking a medical history all the surgical procedures, major and minor, that you have had in the past.

At night I would pray for my husband and my health, asking God to remove all negative thoughts from me. I continued this prayer, asking that I would not lose my leg and appealing for help in remaining positive through this experience. It appeared to me that my head became clear, and I had no negative thoughts regarding my husband. I felt reassured by God. A calming presence came over me. Somehow everything would be okay.

My doctor made arrangements for me to go to New York for the surgery. He called a brace man to prepare a cast with a hinge so that I could bend my leg while sitting on the airplane. Once that was done, I drove myself home with my left leg rather than let anyone know I had been discharged from the hospital.

This was on a Friday when the temperature was thirty or forty degrees below zero. There was ice on the ground, and I had crutches, but I managed to get myself home.

After getting settled, I called my beautician to get my hair cut and styled. Shortly after I had my hair styled, a young man came in wielding a gun and announced, "This is a hold-up! Everybody in the back room!" So I hobbled along, apologizing to the robber for my inability to move fast. He methodically lined us up along the wall, and said, "I don't want anybody's jewelry or credit cards. I want your money. Just give me your money, and nobody will get hurt." Holding a gun to the head of the salon owner, he had her assist him by taking everyone's money. He threatened, "If I hear one sound, she's gonna get it first."

I had planned to go shopping for pajamas and other items to take to the hospital after I left the beauty salon, so I had lots of money which he did not take because it was not in my wallet, but in a special get well card I had received. I still do not know why I had placed the money in the card rather than my purse.

When he had robbed us, he said, "Okay. Now I want everybody in this bathroom." He was demanding that the twenty of us get into a room which would be crowded with five or six people.

We were pushing, trying to stuff ourselves in this little space, so I turned and looked at him and said, "Mister, why don't you line us against the wall until you get out of here because we cannot get into that bathroom, and you need to get out of here while you can."

"Oh. Okay. Line up against the wall," he said.

So, there we were lined up against the wall, and all I could think about was Al Capone's St. Valentine Day Massacre. I was thinking to myself, "We're standing here with our faces to the wall and our backs to him. He could shoot us and keep going."

While I was thinking, I heard him say, "Now I want you to count to one hundred, and I don't want to see one single person's head out this door because I have my lookout man out there, and I'm gonna come back and waste all of you if he sees anyone."

"One, two... twenty-five... eighty... one hundred," and we went and called the police. Then we went to the door, and he was walking down the street like nothing had happened. If the police had come immediately, they would have caught him. But they spent what we considered valuable time asking questions on the telephone. The man could have been out of the country by the time they got there. We consoled each other and we concluded that he had escaped with over a thousand dollars because people were carrying holiday shopping money.

I did not panic when I was faced with death by a robber, nor did I panic when I was diagnosed with cancer, but I was able to assess the situation and figure out what I needed to survive. With the cancer diagnosis I needed to educate and advocate for myself. With the robbery I needed to remain calm, think out the situation, assert myself and pray for safety. I followed my thinking and came out of both situations victoriously.

I got my crutches and stopped by the store on my way home to pick up satin pillowcases to take to the hospital with me. When I got home, a couple of gift-laden friends who had heard I had been discharged from the hospital and was going to New York that Monday had come to cheer me. When I had not responded to the doorbell, they wondered where in the world could I be with so much ice on the streets. They looked across the street and saw me with my crutches and cast - running to greet me and scolding me at the same time. But I had the faith of that tiny mustard seed in the Bible, and I felt that I could move mountains that day.

The next morning, a very, very cold day in Chicago, I left for New York. I just sat on the plane. I refused everything the airline attendants offered. I have no doubt that I was in a state of shock from the robbery and anticipated surgery.

My brother Henry and his family picked me up when I arrived in New York and took me to Memorial Sloan-Kettering Cancer Center. I had never had such a friendly, warm, caring and concerned staff in any hospital experience in my life. My family was right with me. The pre-admission procedures, such as blood work and x-rays, were done prior to my going to the floor or the unit. My family was given a tour of the hospital while I was having the pre-admission work and then joined me in my room. The doctor came in and explained to my family what was going to happen: when I would be taken to the operating room, when the anesthesiologist would come to talk with me, and what medications would be administered to me.

I was a little nervous when I went to the operating room for the surgery. Christmas was past; I was approaching my birthday, and here I was sick. I was pleased that the doctors allowed my family to go in and decorate my room. Balloons were on the wall. Henry had brought champagne. Henry's two-year-old daughter, Annette, sang "Happy Birthday." All the doctors and nurses on the floor came in to help celebrate my birthday.

After the surgery, the doctor asked the nurse to elevate my leg. She just put some pillows under it. When the doctor returned, he was terribly upset. He literally picked up the foot of my bed and said, "THIS IS ELEVATION! This is where I want her leg!" This doctor would understand what some doctors call "attitude." He would have no problem understanding my determination to participate in my medical care.

I have no doubt that prayer played a role. I believe prayer changes things. Years ago when I was being oriented to Chicago and the nursing school, some classmates and I eventually found and attended a neighborhood church, Liberty Baptist Church on South Parkway (now Martin Luther King Drive.) It was about two blocks from school. We would walk there and race back to the school lunch before the cafeteria closed. At other times some of the church members would take us home to eat. After graduation I joined Calvary Baptist Church which was a half-block from where I lived. This is where I started writing monthly medical reports in the church bulletin. I worked in that same community as a professional nurse. My minister, the Rev. Dr. Alfloyd Butler, a Louisianian and Southern University graduate, and I would visit the sick and homebound. He called me the morning of my surgery, and I told him that I had had a personal encounter with God and I knew that everything would work out for me. Indeed, it did.

This was one of so many times I witnessed the power of prayer. I know that when a multitude of people are praying for me, I will get results. Thinking about this reminds me of the breakfast I attended where Bishop Desmond Tutu of South Africa was present. He stated, "My God, there will be a change in South Africa when I see all my sisters and brothers praying all over the world for a change." I am so thankful that I am able to see that change in South Africa. I was happy to see a special on television where physicians acknowledged that many times they prayed for success with their treatments and realized a greater power allowed the healing to take place.

I had an uneventful stay at the hospital, and afterwards I recuperated at my brother Henry's house in New York. His wife, Anne, was very supportive. She worked at their business but took time everyday to prepare meals, launder my clothes and just make me feel welcome. Henry would purchase my medications for me. Little two-year old Annette had a routine. She would drag pillows across the floor so I could elevate my legs, bring my reading glasses, and then deliver the newspapers, tabloids and books that Sara Mayfield had mailed me from Chicago. Throughout the day Annette would look in on me to see that I was comfortable. The support I received from my family and friends played a big role in my healing. After returning to Chicago I spent a whole year with those crutches because bones take a long time to mend.

I decided I wanted to visit my parents; I wanted them to see that I was doing well. I drove from Chicago to Louisiana using my left leg for the gas pedal and brakes. Once they saw me, they were assured that I was going to be okay. However, they were concerned about my driving that distance alone, and without the use of one leg. I didn't tell my parents the whole truth, but my son, Byron, who accompanied me, helped me to drive there,

Henry, Ann and Annette join me at the Americana Hotel, Chicago, for the wedding reception for me and Andrew Gale, 1983.

although he was only twelve at the time. He was a careful driver because I had taught him to drive at an early age.

When I returned to Chicago, I went back to work and did not have any problems. The doctor said my leg would heal completely, "if you do exactly what I tell you to do." I was very careful about following his orders. Every two months I had to have an x-ray of my leg to send to him in New York so that he could see the healing process.

I remember saying, "Can I walk with my cane now?"

"No, Augusta," he said. "I will tell you when to progress to the cane."

I used the cane for about two months before moving on to independent walking. I have no residual effects from that cancer or that surgery. It is extremely important to follow the doctor's instructions. I became a partner with my physician. I had him to understand that I was a human being. I did share with my medical team that I was a registered nurse, and that I wanted to be part of my own care, and they agreed.

Chapter 16

Living In New England

I came from a segregated town: African Americans lived in one part of town, whites in another. Schools were, and I hate this phrase, supposed to be "separate but equal." In that environment, they were separate, but they certainly were not equal. Salem, Massachusetts, in 1987 was totally different. There were very few African Americans there. I'm not sure if many of the people in Salem had ever worked with African Americans or lived close to them. When I moved there, I could see eyes following me, watching me as I walked down the street, as though to say, "Where did she come from? Who is she?"

The institutional barriers of segregation that I knew growing up were not present in Salem, but I felt isolated in the town and at work. I did not see another African American working in that hospital except for a doctor who initially had no interaction with me whatsoever. One day the two of us were on the elevator. I asked him why he was looking at the ceiling of the elevator because the door did not open from the ceiling. He then acknowledged my presence and from that time to this day, we are friends. It was about two and a half years before I saw an African American patient.

I came to Salem from Louisville, Kentucky, where I had moved from Chicago after being recruited to direct a long-term care facility. At this point in my career, I thought I needed a change, to do something differently. I had experience in acute care clinics and health departments, and Byron was away in the Marines, so I had no restrictions.

One day in Louisville I saw an advertisement in the local newspaper "Recruiting Nurses for the New England Area." I thought, "That should be something adventuresome." I had never been to New England. When I responded to the advertisement, I was told immediately that they were looking for staff nurses. I told them I was looking for a management or supervisory posititon. Then about a week later they called asking me to interview for a job in discharge planning.

Shortly afterwards I went to Salem for the interview. I saw no African Americans at the time, and I wondered if I really wanted to go there. So I sat down and listed all the positives and all the negatives about relocating to this part of the country and ended up with only one negative point. And that one negative was there were so few African Americans there.

My "positives" included the opportunity to explore a new area, meet new people, live in an area with a different history, and, very important, receive an increase in salary. I was impressed when I first arrived, and I thought about bringing other African Americans to see this part of the country once I got settled. I was also looking forward to seeing my brother Henry more often since it was only about a four-hour drive to New York.

Salem is a beautiful city, with many historical sites. There is the Pickering House, one of the oldest houses continuously occupied by the same family in America. The graves of a *Mayflower* passenger and Judge John Hawthorne of the Witchcraft trials are in the Salem burying ground. Chestnut Street, one of the most architecurally beautiful streets in the country, and both the Witch Museum and the Peabody Museum are here.

Both black and white people seem very territorial in New England. Many of them spend their entire lives in one area. There are some areas in Massachusetts with large African American populations: Lynn, and Roxbury in Boston, of course. A visitor might not see the segregation – no separate schools, separate facilities, but I experienced some of the invisible barriers of segregation there.

I have been the only African American on many of the jobs that I have had here, particularly in management, so I know what it means to feel isolated in my profession. There's a different kind of behavior toward me than it is for the whites I work with. The team is not really integrated.

In the South we were taught to speak to people, to say "Good Morning," "Good Afternoon," to acknowledge the presence of another person. I don't find that here in New England. Many times I go very cheerfully to work and say good morning to a person there only to have my greeting fall upon a deaf ear. I can recall specifically one morning when a white employee and I were in the dining area. A white man came in and said, "Good Morning." Of course, I turned and said, "Good Morning." He quickly addressed by name the other person who had not said good morning. This was to let me know that he was speaking to the other person and not to me. I have encountered this type incident several times, the little barriers and slights. I realize this is typical of black people's experiences in many parts of our country, and I have experienced my share.

For some time I thought that once I got the job the problem was that people might have been intimidated or unsettled by my qualifications. I came to this part of the country well-prepared, both academically and experientially; therefore, I don't think that achieving my personal or professional goals has been impeded. However, I have come to know I am part of the team in name and skill only. Co-workers have not said but certainly acted as if this is all they want. They need me to do the job. All they want from me are these skills. They want nothing else. They want no interaction. It's strictly work at the office. I hear the whites discuss social meetings to take place after office hours. I finish my work, and it's "I will see you tomorrow."

There was one exception. A young nurse invited me to come to Christmas dinner. We were sitting at the table with four or five other white employees. Looks of shock covered every face there, amazed that she, a white employee, would invite an African American to her house for dinner. She lives in Marblehead, a predominantly white area. That's the only social interaction outside the workplace I've had with white fellow employees.

It has struck me as strange that in all the time I've been here I've not been invited to anything outside of work. Once a manager asked me what I was doing one Easter. She said, "Well, you can come to my house if you have nothing else to do." I did not feel that it was a warm, cordial invitation. I wouldn't invite someone to my home if they have nothing else to do. If I want somebody to come and join me, I say so; I do not qualify the invitation.

Over time I have seen a change in this behavior. I have established a very warm and friendly relationship with the continuing care coordinators and the management team at the Salem Hospital where I am no longer employed.

I desperately wanted to join a black church in the area. After working all week in an all-white setting, I had a yearning to be with my people. I was commuting to Boston (thirty minutes away) every Sunday to go to a black church. One day I was walking down the street in Lynn and saw an African-American woman, Mavis Bennett. I just walked up to her and asked her where black people go to church in this town. She directed me to the Zion Baptist Church. Being new, I got lost the first Sunday and ended up in a black church with an unfamiliar order of service. On the way home I found the church where I had been referred. The next Sunday I attended it. Mavis, who had directed me to Zion had called her friend, Loretta Brinson, who was a member, and Loretta was waiting for me. She introduced herself and took me around to meet almost everybody at the church!

I was impressed by the minister, the Rev. Mr. Walter Murray, Jr., a dynamic young Harvard Divinity School graduate who came to Lynn from Cincinnati, Ohio. He was originally from Nashville, Tennessee. Zion, one of the oldest black Baptist churches in Lynn, was very small and met in an old structure when Rev. Murray came. Some of our parishioners have been at Zion for a long time. Ethel Johnson and Helen Carrington, our oldest parishioners have

Part of Zion Baptist Church family including the Rev. Walter Murray,
James Murray, and Mrs. Donna Murray. I am wearing the big hat. My
friend, Arnold Howe, is standing behind me. Lynn, Massachusetts, 1995.

been members for more than 60 years. Prior to the 1880s a group
of people of African descent came from Nova Scotia and settled
in Lynn.

Zion is like a giant-sized family. It is a place where I go with
a heavy and troubled heart and leave rejoicing. We now have a
multicultural congregation, and we are learning from each other.
We are all sisters and brothers in Christ. We give big hugs at the
close of our morning worship service. Our pastor says we are
expressing love and concern for one another. How I wish I had
had this support when I had my mastectomy!

I have truly been blessed to be a part of this fellowship. I
feel a deep sense of caring, which also helps me to stay focused
on my positive attitude. My pastor, Rev. Murray, has constantly
encouraged me to write this book. Fellow parishioner William
Jones and Rev. Valdasia Merrick never fail to ask about the book

in every encounter. I can only say, "Thank God, that I am a part of the Zion Baptist Church."

During the church's growth some of the younger people, not appreciating history, wanted to purchase an existing church at another location or to tear down the original structure. But there were strong people who were determined to preserve that part of African American history and heritage. Consequently, the original building is still standing although an extension has been added.

In addition to enlarging the sanctuary, the pastor envisioned instituting several outreach community programs. Despite my being a new parishioner, he graciously permitted me to publish a quarterly "Medical Watch" in the bulletin which includes health information. This allows the parishioners an opportunity to become educated on some health issues. The church helps the teenagers in Lynn with weekly tutoring and programs which teach them about Christianity and various aspects of life and steward-

My niece, Annette, on a tour of historic Newport, Rhode Island mansions with me (center) and Zion church member Gladys Henderson, 1994.

ship. The youngsters can also come in and speak with our associate ministers, the Rev. Ms. Valdasia Merrick, the Rev. Ms. Adrienne Berry-Long, the Rev. William Hill and the Rev. Leonard Maxwell. Rev. Murray successfully established a coalition of several Lynn churches of various denominations to assist with crime and youth-related problems, housing and education. We are looking forward to retiring the mortgage on our church so that we will have more money for additional outreach programs, perhaps a program for senior members of the community, maybe a lunch program, and a nursing home. We currently have computer classes for adults and an outreach ministry serving meals and furnishing clothing to the homeless.

Chapter 17

Some Reflections

My fiftieth birthday was very special for me. I had lived half a century and was a three-year breast cancer survivor at that time. Byron was so happy to be with me, and he still carries a picture in his wallet of me wearing a mini dress that weekend. He wanted to make sure I used my pump every night to control swelling in my arm. He would even come in and put my arm up and turn the pump on and say, "Okay, Mom, it's time for your pump."

My church family was involved in the celebration: Delores Harris and Virginia Peacock planned the event, and a committee headed by Rochelle Bluefort prepared the food which was fit for royalty. Family members and friends came from Illinois, California, New York,

Byron teased me about the mini-skirt when he came to help celebrate my 50th birthday. Salem, 1991. Photograph by Bill Upshaw.

Connecticut, Maryland, and Michigan to help me celebrate. Since many of the people who attended were around my age, I think they felt that they were celebrating their 50th birthday, too. The affair was unforgettable.

I am now older than my mother was when she died. She knew some months before she passed that she was dying. She was alone; her husband, Dr. Harry Osibin, a dentist, died in the early 1960s. I spent a month with her before she died. I don't recall her ever being orderly about her business, but she had prepared for her death. Whenever she told me to look somewhere to get something, it was always there. When she asked me to do something, she could tell me exactly how to do it. I think this was her means of letting me know about her business and affairs.

With Byron at 50th birthday celebration attended by 125 relatives and friends from around the country. Knights of Columbus Hall, Salem, 1991. Photograph by Bill Upshaw.

Items in her drawers were neatly arranged. I was surprised to find in plain view the divorce papers – at least forty years old – from my father.

She asked a question that I'll never forget: "Are you angry with me?"

"About what?" I asked her.

"About me divorcing your father and not spending time with you as you were growing up," she said. She was setting her business straight, seeking peace of mind.

"Of course, I am not angry with you." I said, "Let's enjoy what we have right now, the time we have together now."

She was slipping into a coma, and this ace nurse was not cognizant of it. I just didn't want it to happen although I knew ultimately that her condition was terminal. Her sleeping a lot did not alarm me. I remember telling her one day, "If you stay out of bed an hour or so, I'll stay here another week with you." Talk about determination. My mother got out of the bed, and I took her outside of the house for a walk. She stopped and, I thought, was going to sleep outside of the house, but she was steadily becoming comatose. She was determined to spend her last moments with me.

Essentially, breast cancer treatment has not improved a great deal over the last twenty-five years. Our mothers received radiation or chemotherapy, the standard kinds of therapy still used today. We are constantly hearing about research and getting funds for research projects. What is being researched? Mastectomy? Are they researching chemotherapy, radiation? We know the effects of both. There's just not been that much improvement in treatment, cure, and prevention in breast cancer due to lack of necessary funds for research, and I strongly feel the lack of direction for the research. A multi-disciplinary approach which looks at all the factors seems to be the most effective strategy. The team would consist of an epidemologist, a nutritionist, a microbiologist, chemist, pharmacist, oncologist, a nurse, and an environmental specialist who could look at the effect of the ocean, sea, wind, chemicals and chemical dump sites. We need experts from around the world since breast cancer is a pandemic occurrence. The researchers should address and look at questions that have been raised about breast cancer, such as "Why is it that when women move to various locations they take up the breast cancer statistics of that location? Some studies indicate that there is either an increase or decrease in breast cancer of the migrant group corresponding to that of the local population. It is certainly not the case that women were earmarked with breast cancer and just move to these areas.

As my friend, constant supporter and breast cancer activist Lise Beane says, "The brain cannot answer questions that are not asked of it. We must ask the right questions and tenaciously seek the right answers. It will take a lot of people putting their minds together to solve the cause and prevention of breast cancer."

I have a personal survivor's prayer I was asked to write for one of my Breast Cancer Support Groups. I seriously thought about this request. I turned back the hand on the clock of time remembering what I was thankful for and came up with this prayer.

Survivor's Prayer

God, we thank you for this day
Our family, friends and support groups
Help us to forget the pains of yesterday
Help us to relax and to realize we are
Beautiful and very precious.

At home in Salem wearing my golden anniversary mini-dress and holding my mother's picture during the celebration of my 50th birthday and life and triumph over breast cancer, 1991. Some of the 50th birthday candles, plus "one to grow on" are visible behind me. Photograph by Bill Upshaw.

My breast cancer has allowed me to help in a way I never dreamed; the little girl who said she wanted to be a nurse got her wish. I published the *Ebony* article to impart information I had been sharing with family, friends, small groups, and church folks to a broader audience. It was not my intent to do the article for publicity or for people to contact me. I did it as an educational effort. That was my primary concern. But after the article was published I had a better idea of how I had helped. I heard from people from many places, as far away as India. I received a lot of mail from prisoners happy to see a black woman doing articles of this type. The very first call I received was from a woman in Tennessee who indicated to me that she had just had a mastectomy and was home when *Ebony* was strategically placed near her comfortable chair. She said, "The magazine was just there, and I picked it up and was thumbing through it when I saw this black woman on a full page. Then I saw the title and read it. I told my husband, 'I am going to contact this woman if it takes every penny I own. I want to talk with this woman.'" Salem Hospital, where I was employed, was mentioned in the article, so she called there and spoke with me. She knew that breast cancer was not a death sentence. She was so happy that she had seen a black woman express how she felt about having breast cancer and how she coped and survived. She said that it gave her much encouragement and inspiration. "Before reading that article I had gotten comfortable with just dying," she said. "After I read the article, I have a new life, and I just wanted to thank you for that."

After I had the surgery, I too have a new life, and I thank God for that. People are living longer with cancer, but the number of new cases every year is frightfully high. There needs to be more research to seek causes and cures of this dreadful disease. My questions remain: Why did my mother die from breast cancer? Why did I, her daughter, contract breast cancer? Why?

Perhaps this book will be read by a person who will make a breakthrough in breast cancer treatment. At any rate, my hope is that a breakthrough will come soon. For the readers with cancer or who have had mastectomies or lumpectomies, my wish is that this account of my experiences will enlighten you and give you hope for the future.

BREAST CANCER INFORMATION AND SUPPORT SOURCES

American Association of Retired Persons (AARP)
Seeks to encourage older women to be screened regularly for breast cancer. Provides information, including some brochures, and screenings in some local communities. Write to AARP's Breast Care Campaign - NB, Health Advocacy Services, 601 E Street, Northwest, Washington, D. C. 20049.

American Cancer Society
General information for cancer patients and their families. Phone 1-800-ACS-2345 (1-800-227-1234) or nearest office listed in your local phone directory.

American College of Radiology
Information on questions relating to mammography or radiation treatment. Phone (703)648-8910.

American Indian Healthcare Association
Provides information about cancer and treatment options. (303)607-1048.

Asian and Pacific Islander American Health Forum
Promotes cancer awareness through education and information relating to treatment choices. (415) 541-0866.

Avon's Breast Cancer Awareness Crusade
Corporate sponsor which funds over 100 community-based breast cancer programs.

Breast Cancer Action Group
Outreach and educational organization actively seeking art and writing submissions for its "Healing Legacies" collection from women who have had breast cancer. Two Church Street, 3rd floor, P. O. Box 5605, Burlington, Vt., 05402. FAX: (802)863-3140; Phone (802) 863-3507.

Breast Cancer Fund
Seeks to raise awareness, finance education, advocacy, support, research, early detection and treatment projects. 1280 Columbus Avenue, Suite 201, Dept. P, San Francisco, CA 94133.

Breast Cancer Resource Center
Information and support services. 1765 "N" Street, Northwest, Washington, D. C. 20036.

Cancer Information Services Hot Line
Information and treatment options for people of color. 1-800-4-CANCER; (422-6237). National Cancer Society.

Celebrating Life Foundation
Promotes charitable efforts to advance knowledge and awareness of the risk and prevention of breast cancer among African American women and other women of color. 3001 LBJ Freeway, Suite 131, Dallas TX 75234, (214) 243-3935.

Expedition Inspiration
High altitude mountain climbing to raise funds for the Breast Cancer Fund.

Group Support Programs
Some locales have specific breast cancer support groups. Most urban areas have cancer support groups for patients and families which meet regularly to share experiences and coping mechanisms. Call local branch of American Cancer Society.

I Can Cope
Series of classes conducted by health care professionals and others to provide factual information and encouragement to cancer patients and families. Sponsored by American Cancer Society.

Look Good, Feel Better
Conducted by trained volunteers to provide guidance and instruction to women to foster renewed confidence and self-esteem while recovering from cancer treatment. Co-sponsored by the American Cancer Society and the Cosmetic, Toiletry and Fragrance Association Foundation and the National Cosmetology Association.

National Alliance of Breast Cancer Organizations
Information on mammography, breast cancer and how to find a local facility. 9 East 37th Street, 10th Floor, New York, NY 10016.

National Black Leadership Initiative on Cancer
Information on cancer education and treatment. (202) 806-5659.

National Cancer Institute
Information line 1-800-4-CANCER (1-800-422-6237)

National Cancer Institute Publications
A large number of booklets about cancer are available in several languages. A few are listed in the bibliography which follows this section. Call the information number above for additional titles.

National Coalition for Cancer Survivorship
Organization of cancer survivors. 1010 Wayne Avenue, 5th Floor, Silver Spring, MD 20910, (301)650-8868.

National Hispanic Leadership Initiative on Cancer/En Accion
Provides cancer education and treatment information. (301)496-8680.

National Lymphedema Network
Education, general information, support and referrals about lymphedema and treatment choices. Phone 1-800-541-3259.

Office of Minority Health Resource Center
Makes available information on education and treatment of cancer. 1-800-444-6472.

Reach to Recovery
Visitation program which provides support to women who have breast cancer or are recovering from treatment. A trained volunteer may be requested at any phase of the breast cancer experience. Sponsored by the American Cancer Society.

Road to Recovery
Volunteer program to provide cancer patients with transportation to and from treatment. Sponsored by the American Cancer Society.

Share: Self-Help for Women with Breast and Ovarian Cancer
Support group offering hotline information in English and Spanish in the
New York area. (212) 719-0364, 19 West 44th Street, New York, NY 10036.
English hotline (212)382-2111; Spanish hotline (212)719-4454.

Sisters Breast Cancer Survivors' Network
African American information network for cancer survivors dedicated to
providing support to women in underserved communities. Also seeks tax-
deductible contributions made to Community Partners F.B.O. Sisters. 3119
W. 59th street, #3, Los Angeles, CA 90043. (213)293-9408 or (213)234-
7762; FAX (213)730-8155.

Sisters Network
National support group which seeks to empower African American breast
cancer survivors and to increase local and national awareness of the impact
of breast cancer in the African American community. National headquarters, 8787 Woodway Drive, Suite 4207, Houston, TX 77063. (713)781-0255.

Susan G. Komen Breast Cancer Foundation
National organization which provides information about cancer and treatment options.
1-800-I'M Aware (462-9273)

Y-ME Men's Hotline
Seeks to educate men to encourage the women in their lives to have regular
examinations. To receive copy of "When the Woman You Love Has Breast
Cancer," write to Y-ME, 212 West Van Buren-Box PB, Chicago, Ill 60607;
1-800-221-2141.

**Y-ME National Organization for Breast
Cancer Information and Support, Inc.**
Independent support groups. 24-hour hotline (312)986-8228; Central Time
zone between 9 am and 5 pm, 1-800-221-2141.

SELECTED BIBLIOGRAPHY

AARP. *Chances Are - You Need A Mammogram: A Guide for Midlife and Older Women.* Stock number D15402. AARP Fulfillment (EE0864). Washington: 1994.

Abbott, Dorothy. *Nothing's Changed: Diary of A Mastectomy.* New York: F. Fell Publishers, c1981.

Altman, Roberta. *Waking Up, Fighting Back: The Politics of Breast Cancer.* Boston: Little, Brown, 1996.

Baron-Faust, Rita. *Breast Cancer: What Every Woman Should Know.* New York: Hearst Books, c1995.

Berger, Karen and Bostwick, John III. *A Woman's Decision: Breast Care, Treatment, and Reconstruction.* St. Louis, Quality Medical Publishing, 1994.

Boyd, Peggy. *The Silent Wound: A Startling Report on Breast Cancer and Sexuality.* Reading, Mass.: Addison-Wesley Publishers, 1984.

Dackman, Linda. Up Front: Sex and the Post-Mastectomy Woman. New York: Penguin Books, 1990.

Davidson, James A. and Winebrenner, Jan. *In Touch With Your Breasts: The Answer to Women's Questions About Breast Care.* Waco: WRS Publishing, 1995.

Dawson, Deborah A. *Breast Cancer Risk Factors and Screening:* United States. U.S. Department of Health, 1990

Dunnavant, Sylvia and Egiebor, Sharon, editors. *Celebrating Life: African American Women Speak Out About Breast Cancer.* Dallas: USFI, 1995.

Feldman, Gayle. *You Don't Have to be Your Mother*. New York: W. W. Norton, c1994.

Ferguson, Pamela. *The Self/Shiatsu Handbook, Breast Cancer Exercise*. New York. Perigee Publishing, 1995.

Graham, Jory. *In The Company of Others*. Harcourt Brace Jovanavich, c1982.

Greenberg, Mimi, Ph.D. Invisible Scars: *A Guide to Coping With the Emotional Impact of Breast Cancer*. New York: St. Martins Press, 1988.

Halbert, David S. *Your Breast and You: What Every Woman Needs to Know About Breast Diseases, Breast Cancer and Cosmetic Breast Surgery Before She Has A Problem*. Abilene: Askon Publishing Company, c1985.

Hirshaut, Yashar and Pressman, Peter I. *Breast Cancer: The Complete Guide*. New York: Bantam Books, 1992.

Instituto Nacional del Cancer. *Tiene 50 a~nos de edad o mas? Un Mamograma Podria Salvarle a vida*. Bethesda: Publicacion del N.H., numero 94-3418[s], Institutos Nacionale de la Salud, 1994.

Instuto Nacional del Cancer. *Lo Que Usted Debe Saber Sobre Los Examenes de Los Senos*. Publicacion del NIH; numero 92-2000S, Bethesda:. Instituto Nacional del Cancer.

Kahane, Deborah Hobler. *No Less A Woman: Femininity, Sexuality and Breast Cancer*. Alameda: Hunter House, 1995.

Karmonicky, Lydia and Rosenberg, Anne with Betancourt, Marian. *What to Do If You Get Breast Cancer: Two Breast Cancer Specialists Help You Take Charge and Make Informed Choices*. Boston: Little, Brown, c1995.

Kuehn, Paul. *Breast Care Options: A Cancer Specialist Discusses Breast Care Options, Risk Factors, and How To Cope With Breast Cancer*. South Windsor, Connecticut: Newmark Publishing Company, c1986.

LaTour, Kathy. *The Breast Cancer Companion: From Diagnosis, Through Treatment/ Everything You Need to Know for Every Step Along the Way to Recovery.* New York: William Morrow and Company, c1993.

Lorde, Audre. *The Cancer Journals.* Argyle, New York: Spinsters, Ink, 1980.

Love, Susan M. and Lindsey, Karen. *Dr. Susan Love's Breast Book.* Reading, Massachusetts: Addison-Wesley, 1991.

Mayer, Musa. *Examining Myself: One Woman's Story of Breast Cancer Treatment.* London and Boston: Faber and Faber, 1993.

National Cancer Institute. *The Breast Cancer Digest: A Guide to Medical Care, Emotional Support, Educational Programs and Resources.* DHEW Publication, number [NIH] 79-1691. U.S. Department of Health, 1979.

National Cancer Institute. *I Promise To Schedule Regular Mammograms Beginning at Age 50.* Poster, U. S. Department of Health., 1994.

Pederson, Lucille M. and Janet M. Trigg. *Breast Cancer: A Family Survival Guide.* Westport, Connecticut: Bergin and Garvey, 1995.

Robinson, Rebecca Y. and Petrek, Jeanne A. *A Step-by-Step Guide to Dealing With Your Breast Cancer.* Secaucus, New Jersey: Carol Publishing Group, 1994.

Runowicz, Carolyn D. and Haupt, Donna. *To Be Alive: A Woman's Guide to A Full Life After Cancer.* New York: Holt, c1995.

Schindler, Lydia Woods. *A Health Guide for All Women: Understanding Breast Changes, NIH Publication, number 93-3536.* Bethesda: National Institutes, 1993.

Snyder, Marilyn. *An Informed Decision: Understanding Breast Reconstruction.* New York: M. Evans and Company, c1984.

Soffa, Virginia M. *The Journey Beyond Breast Cancer: From the Personal to the Political: Taking an Active Role in Prevention, Diagnosis, and Your Own Healing*. Rochester, Vermont: Healing Arts Press, c1994.

Stone, Barbara E. *Cancer as Initiation: Surviving The Fire: A Guide For Living With Cancer for Patient, Provider, Spouse, Family or Friend*. Chicago: Open Court, c1994.

Stumm, Diana. *Recovering After Breast Surgery: Exercises to Strengthen Your Body and Relieve Pain*. Alameda: Hunter House, c1995.

Swirsky, Joan. *The Breast Cancer Handbook: Taking Control After You Find A Lump*. New York: HarperPerennial, 1994.

Vigna, Judith. *When Eric's Mom Fought Cancer*. Morton Grove, Illinois: A. Whitman, 1993.

Virag, Irene. *We're All In This Together: Families Facing Breast Cancer*. Kansas: Andrews and McMeel, 1995.

Wilson-Hashiguchi, Clo. *Stealing the Dragon's Fire: A Personal Guide and Handbook For Dealing With Breast Cancer*. Bothell, Washington: Wilson Publishing, c1995.

INDEX

A

A Sense of Balance 42
Abdomen 38
Abdominal 38
Ackward, the Rev. Russell 73
Adjuvant therapy 36-37
Alabama 59, 86
American Cancer Society 51, 54, 63, 64, 66, 67
American Medical Association 55
Anesthesiologist 39
Anxiety 21, 49
Aspiration, of fluid, 27, 28
    in childhood 77, 79, 123
Awards 88

B

Black women, death from breast cancer 9, 11
    incidence of breast cancer in 11
Beane, Lise 50, 122
Bennett, Mavis 115
Berry, Byron Barrington 31, 32, 104, 109, 112, 119, 120
    Victor 93, 98
Bethune, Mary McLeod 79
Billings Hospital 93
Biopsy 16
Bluefort, Rochelle 119
Bone marrow transplant 68
Bowman, Wilma-Gene 74
Breast cancer
    diagnosis 11
    incidence 9
    support group 50